discovering

JAMES JOYCE

THE UNIVERSITY AT BUFFALO COLLECTION

James Joyce and Sylvia Beach standing in the doorway of
Shakespeare and Company, 1921.

discovering
JAMES JOYCE

THE UNIVERSITY AT BUFFALO COLLECTION

James Joyce seated, playing guitar, Zurich, 1915.

This catalogue was published on the occasion of the exhibition *Discovering James Joyce: The University at Buffalo Collection,* organized by the Poetry Collection of the University at Buffalo Libraries, the University Art Galleries, and the School of Architecture and Planning.

library.buffalo.edu/jamesjoyce

EXHIBITION DATES

UB Anderson Gallery
One Martha Jackson Place
Buffalo, NY 14214

June 13, 2009–September 13, 2009

EXHIBITION CREDITS

Exhibition Curator: Michael Basinski
Assistant Curator: James Maynard
Director of Music & Special Collections: Nancy Nuzzo
Director of UB Art Galleries: Sandra H. Olsen
Dean, School of Architecture and Planning: Brian Carter
Designers: Paul Dudkowski, Daniel Stripp, and Dan Chorley
Curator of Education: Ginny O'Brien Lohr
Finance & General Operations Manager: Jennifer Markee
Registrar & Collections Manager: Robert Scalise
Preparators: Ken Short and Tim Roby
Technology Coordinator: Jim Snider
Building Maintenance: Paul Wilcox

CATALOGUE CREDITS

Essayists: Oscar A. Silverman, Luca Crispi, Michael Groden, and Sam Slote
Editor: James Maynard
Designer: Kristopher Miller
Photographer: James A. Ulrich
Print Management: Kristopher Miller

Front cover: Detail of Patrick Tuohy's portrait of James Joyce, circa 1924
Back cover: Detail of *Sporting Times* poster advertising "The Scandal of *Ulysses*"

All quotations from Sylvia Beach's papers used with the permission of her estate

Printed in an edition of 1,000 copies in 2009
Second printing in 2016

The Poetry Collection
420 Capen Hall
Buffalo, NY 14260

UB University at Buffalo The State University of New York

THE JAMES JOYCE COLLECTION WAS ESTABLISHED
WITH THE GENEROUS SUPPORT OF:

MARGARETTA F. WICKSER IN MEMORY OF PHILIP J. WICKSER
CONSTANCE W. STAFFORD AND WALTER F. STAFFORD, JR.
B. W. HUEBSCH
MRS. SPENCER KITTINGER
FRIENDS OF THE LOCKWOOD MEMORIAL LIBRARY

THE EXHIBITION AND CATALOGUE HAVE BEEN
MADE POSSIBLE BY GIFTS FROM:

CONSTANCE W. STAFFORD CHARITABLE TRUST
WALTER AND CONSTANCE CONSTANTINE
THE BAIRD FOUNDATION
THE GLADYS KRIEBLE DELMAS FOUNDATION
THE JOHN R. OISHEI FOUNDATION
JOAN AND LOUIS SLOVINSKY
DAVID AND NANCY NUZZO
THE EMERALD BALL
MORTIMER SPILLER
THE DAVID GRAY CHAIR OF POETRY AND LETTERS (STEVE McCAFFERY)
GAYLORD BROS.
DONALD ELICK
KEVIN AND CHERYL ALBAUGH
MR. AND MRS. THOMAS KNAB

ADDITIONAL SUPPORT PROVIDED BY:

UNIVERSITY AT BUFFALO LIBRARIES
UNIVERSITY AT BUFFALO ART GALLERIES
UNIVERSITY AT BUFFALO SCHOOL OF ARCHITECTURE AND PLANNING
UNIVERSITY AT BUFFALO OFFICE OF THE VICE PRESIDENT FOR RESEARCH

James Joyce standing beside greenhouse, Dublin, 1904. Photograph by Constantine P. Curran.

CONTENTS

James Joyce in cap, Bognar, Wales, 1923.

FOREWORD & ACKNOWLEDGMENTS:
JAMES JOYCE IN BUFFALO, NEW YORK

Michael Basinski, Curator of the Poetry Collection

The Poetry Collection of the University at Buffalo stands alone as a singular research library for the scholarly study of poetry after 1900. As poetry's library of record, the Poetry Collection offers a comprehensive account of poetry's evolution over the last one hundred and ten years. This historical unfolding is an interconnected and symbiotic imaginative procession where poets, writers, and communities of writers and artists create both in conflict with each other and in harmony, and it involves, in fact relies upon, the entrepreneurial spirit and pure tenacity and faith of editors and publishers who consistently face scorn and hardship to publish and disseminate new writing. To harvest in this realm of writing, the Poetry Collection's foundation is a simple yet expansive collecting policy that mandates that all published poetry must be equally represented from the most sacred to the most profane. The collection's expanse—140,000 monograph titles, including 6,600 broadsides; 9,000 runs of little literary magazines; 150 named manuscript collections—defines the extent of that fact. UB's Poetry Collection is the largest in North America, and, while there are many peaks in this marvelous array, there is only one pinnacle, and that crown jewel is the James Joyce Collection.

James Joyce was born on February 2, 1882 in Dublin. On June 16, 1904, Joyce and Nora Barnacle went on their first date. This June date, now known as Bloomsday, was immortalized and celebrated in Joyce's *Ulysses*. In May of 1907 Elkin Matthews published Joyce's small collection of poems titled *Chamber Music*. *Dubliners* and *A Portrait of the Artist as a Young Man* followed. On February 2, 1922, Sylvia Beach, through the vehicle of her bookstore, Shakespeare and Company, published *Ulysses*. A year later Joyce began to compose a text he initially called *Work in Progress*. In May of 1939 *Work in Progress* was published as *Finnegans Wake*. In late 1940, escaping the impending Nazi occupation of Paris, Joyce and his family fled to Zurich. Joyce died there on January 13, 1941 and was buried in the Fluntern Cemetery. To meet expenses, in 1949 Joyce's family exhibited a large selection of Joyce memorabilia and manuscript material at the La Hune Gallery in Paris.

Oscar Silverman, a member of the English Department of the University of Buffalo (as it was known until 1962 when it became the University at Buffalo, the State University of New York), visited the exhibition and recognized the intellectual significance of the materials on display. Silverman realized that a Joyce archive in the Poetry Collection would fit into the sprawling networks of twentieth-century writing and give rise to scholarship for generations. Returning to Buffalo, Silverman informed Charles D. Abbott, first director of the University Libraries, about the availability of the Joyce Collection. Abbott had founded the Poetry Collection in 1937 and was an early proponent of manuscript studies. Together, they paved the road for Joyce's journey to Western New York. However, this interdepartmental liaison is only the beginning of the story.

The James Joyce Collection came to the Poetry Collection, in no small measure, because of the foresight and generosity of friends of the University of Buffalo. In 1950 a gift from Margaretta F. Wickser, made in memory of her husband Philip J. Wickser, brought the La Hune consignment of Joyce materials to the Poetry Collection, including manuscripts, notebooks, letters, and Joyce's private library, which included books inscribed to Joyce from William Butler Yeats, Ezra Pound, Nancy Cunard, Ernest Hemingway, James Stevens, and T. S. Eliot. Among the paintings that arrived in this installment were portraits of James Joyce and Joyce's father, John Stanislaus Joyce, by world-renowned Irish painter Patrick Tuohy; two portraits of Nora Joyce; and five oils of Joyce's distant relatives. Joyce's famous walking sticks, glasses, and passports were also part of this consignment.

Thanks to Constance and Walter Stafford's hands-on negotiations in Paris and their financial support, Joyce materials were subsequently purchased from Sylvia Beach, publisher of the first edition of *Ulysses*, in 1959. The Sylvia Beach consignment included Joyce's first *Portrait of the Artist* notebook; inscribed photographs; her extensive correspondence with Maurice Darantiere, whose printing firm typeset *Ulysses*; her correspondence with Joyce translators and publishers like Harry and Caresse Crosby of Black Sun Press; and letters that James Joyce wrote to her before and after the publication of *Ulysses*. Sylvia Beach's personal James Joyce book collection also came to UB. Among her treasures was her personally inscribed copy of *Ulysses*, in which Joyce's poem, "Who is Sylvia," is tipped in, as was Joyce's schema for *Ulysses*, which outlined some of the complexities Joyce included as he structured his novel. Beach's copy, number 2 of 100 printed on Dutch hand-made paper, is one of the most magnificent association copies in the world. Among the other unique items in this consignment were lists of possible subscribers to *Ulysses* in Joyce's hand, the final color proof of the Greek blue *Ulysses* paper cover, and a stack of completed order forms from notables such as T. E. Lawrence, Samuel Roth, Djuna Barnes, William Carlos Williams, and Peggy Guggenheim.

B. W. Huebsch, an American publisher and an associate of Joyce, donated further materials in 1951 and 1959. Another installment arrived after the death of Sylvia Beach in 1962, again through the support of the Staffords, the generosity of Mrs. Spencer Kittinger, and the Friends of the Lockwood Memorial Library. Finally, in 1968, an acquisition of *Finnegans Wake* uncut and heavily revised page proofs from Maria Jolas completed the manuscript collection. In the last few decades, a collection of translations of Joyce's novels, short stories, and poems has been added. *Ulysses*, for example, can be read in more than twenty languages. To be inclusive, virtually all Joyce criticism is collected along with new editions of Joyce's books and novels.

Comprising more than 10,000 pages of manuscript material, notebooks, and letters, the University at Buffalo's James Joyce Collection is the most prestigious and

Poster advertising *Exposition en Hommage à James Joyce*, Paris, 1949.

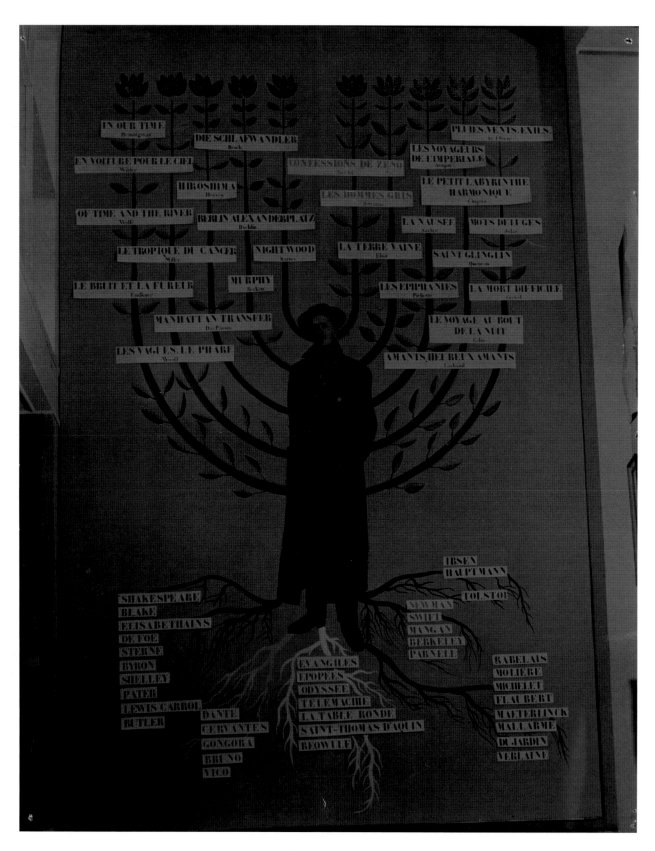

La Hune Gallery exhibition panel illustrating Joyce's place in literary history.

largest Joyce collection in the world. From the time the various Joyce consignments arrived at the Poetry Collection, the manuscripts, notebooks, and ephemeral items have been in full use. They still are today, as the world of Joyce scholarship knows UB's Joyce Collection quite well. This collection, however, has a greater appeal to other audiences. Joyce's ranking as one of the twentieth century's greatest artists and *Ulysses* as the greatest literary achievement of the twentieth century have drawn attention from all quarters.

Discovering what to exhibit and where and how to display various items was a challenge. The depth and breadth of the collection had to be addressed without exhibiting several miles of manuscripts. The research value of the collection had to be revealed without listing more than one hundred books the archive has supported. The author behind the art had to emerge as pan-European. Furthermore, the compromised state of the notebooks, manuscripts, and proofs was an issue; many of them are near one hundred years old and in need of conservation. The list of considerations was a labyrinth, and each item in the exhibition had to pass muster. Overall, the greatest challenge of this project was to create an exhibition that would reintroduce the intellectual opportunities available in the James Joyce Collection to the Joyce scholarly community and also introduce UB's James Joyce Collection to an ever-expanding public.

Meeting these challenges involved intense cooperation among the Poetry Collection and University Libraries, the UB Art Galleries, and the School of Architecture and Planning. Working across disciplines, Nancy Nuzzo, Director of Music & Special Collections, and I teamed with Sandra Olsen, Director of UB Art Galleries, and Brian Carter, Dean of the School of Architecture and Planning. We applied for and received an Interdisciplinary Research Development Fund grant from the office of Jorge V. José, Vice President for Research. This grant allowed our working committee to obtain a conservation report from the Northeast Document Conservation Center and to invite Joyce scholars Sam Slote and Michael Groden to Buffalo to assist in the exhibition planning. Our working group, including our students, variously involved members from all across the UB campuses. The design of the exhibition on the work of James Joyce was prepared by graduate students in the architecture program at UB. Working under the direction of Brian Carter, and in collaboration with UB Anderson Gallery staff, M.Arch students Paul Dudkowski, Daniel Stripp, and Dan Chorley developed design proposals with Sandra Olsen and went on to fabricate the installation with UB Anderson Gallery staff members Robert Scalise and Ken Short. These initiatives highlighted this project as an invaluable educational program that focused on the aims of UB2020 by integrating architecture, scholarly research, inter-disciplinary collaborations, material studies, and innovative design. Each individual brought input and expertise to this project.

Years ago, it seems, during those sleepless nights when I began considering this exhibition, I never, never imagined that so many good UB citizens would contribute. They did. Without the administration, faculty, staff, and students of UB, the James Joyce Collection, truly a literary wonder of the world, would not be on view. In support of the University's ongoing commitment to education, research, and development, the

Poetry Collection invites one and all to open their intellect and imagination and in the spirit of wonder and exploration enjoy the James Joyce Collection.

Without the help of many individuals this exhibition in all its many facets would not have been possible. I join my colleagues Nancy Nuzzo, Sandra Olsen, and Brian Carter in thanking the following individuals for their generous and expert assistance (all affiliations are with the University at Buffalo except where noted): Ana Alba, Cynthia Albertson, and Katrina Bartlett, graduate students, Art Conservation Department, Buffalo State College; April Bialecki; Ruth Bryant, Assistant Dean, School of Architecture and Planning; Melanie Buhrmaster-Bunch, Director of Corporate Relations; Barbara Carlson, Assistant to the Dean, School of Architecture and Planning; Dan Chorley; Dr. Barbara Cole, Education Director, Just Buffalo Literary Center, Buffalo, NY; Dr. Luca Crispi, Lecturer in the School of English, Drama, and Film and in the University College Dublin Centre for Research for James Joyce Studies; Ronan Crowley; John DellaContrada, Senior Director of Media Relations, University Communications; Amy Loucks-DiMatteo, Manager of Library Network Support, University Libraries; Patricia Donovan, Senior Editor, University Communications; Paul Dudkowski; Catherine Dunning, Mary Barnard Fellow, the Poetry Collection; Donald Elick, Director of Development, University Libraries; Megan Faragher; Ron Gaczewski, Preservation Officer, University Libraries; Joshua Gordon; Dr. Michael Groden, Distinguished University Professor, Department of English, the University of Western Ontario; Professor James Hamm, Art Conservation Department, Buffalo State College; Patricia Hamm, Fine Arts Conservation and Technical Services, Clarence Center, NY; Jeannie Hoag, Mary Barnard Fellow, the Poetry Collection; Thomas P. Honan, Director of Foundation Relations; Dr. Mara Huber, Special Assistant to the President for Educational Initiatives and Director of Community Partnerships; Alexander Clark Johnston; Isidor Justeson, Mary Barnard Fellow, the Poetry Collection; Dr. Damien Keane, Department of English; Jason Kovari; Erika Ledermann; Ginny O'Brien Lohr, Curator of Education, UB Anderson Gallery; Jennifer Markee, Finance and Operations Manager, UB Art Galleries; Dr. James Maynard, Visiting Assistant Curator, the Poetry Collection; William McDonnell, Associate Dean, School of Architecture and Planning; Deborah McKinzie, Associate Vice President for Development, College of Arts and Sciences; Dr. Cristanne C. Miller, Chair, Department of English; Kristopher Miller, Interactive Graphic Designer, University Libraries; Karen Walton Morse, Processing Archivist, University Archives; Walter Newman, Director of Paper Conservation, Northeast Document Conservation Center, Andover, MA; William Offhaus, Special Collections Assistant, University Archives; Peggy Pajak, Reformatting Technician, Preservation Program, University Libraries; Stephen Roberts, Associate Vice President for University Libraries; Tim Roby, Assistant Preparator, UB Art Galleries; Robert Scalise, Registrar and Collections Manager, UB Art Galleries; Dr. Mark Shechner, Department of English; Ken Short, Head Preparator, UB Art Galleries; Dr. Sam Slote, Lecturer, Department of English, Trinity College, University of Dublin; Dan Stripp;

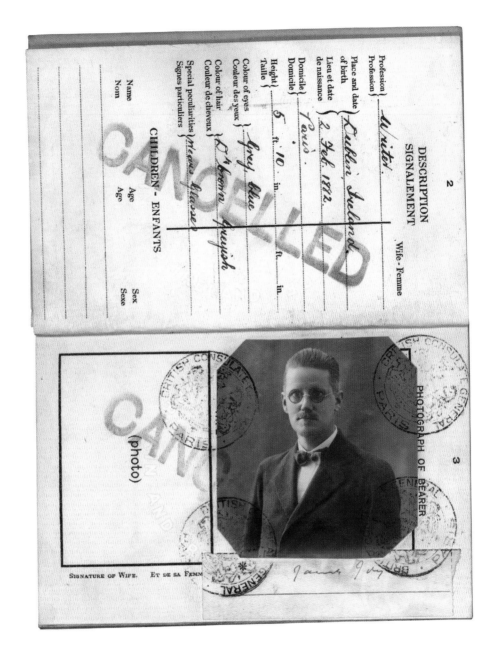

James Joyce's British passport, issued May 3, 1924.

Guy Tomassi, Director of Development, College of Arts and Sciences; Donald J. Trainor, Jr., Media Designer/Consultant, Visual Media Services, ITSS, Academic Services, CIT; Christopher Trybus; James A. Ulrich, Photographer, Visual Media Services, ITSS, Academic Services, CIT; Kim Wagner, Conservation Technician, Preservation Program, University Libraries; Diane Marie Ward, Principal Poetry Cataloguer, the Poetry Collection; Paul Wilcox, Building Maintenance, UB Anderson Gallery; Dennis Wisniewski, Avenue Art & Frame, Buffalo, NY; Nancy Wulbrecht, former Registrar, UB Art Galleries; Penelope Wyatt, Wyatt Design, Buffalo, NY; and Dick Yencer, Manager of Materials and Methods Shop, School of Architecture and Planning.

WHY BUFFALO?: JAMES JOYCE: PARIS-BUFFALO:
THE JOYCE COLLECTIONS AT THE LOCKWOOD MEMORIAL LIBRARY*

Oscar A. Silverman

In the fall of 1949, on a sabbatical leave, I, with hundreds of other people, went a number of times to see the exhibition of books, manuscripts, memorabilia, etc., of the late James Joyce, who had died in 1941. The exhibition was held in a famous bookshop on the left bank of Paris called Librairie La Hune—a first-rate modern bookstore quite near the church of St. Germain-des-Prés. The exhibition was brilliantly arranged: one was struck immediately by a pictorial map (fig. 1) showing the progress of Leopold Bloom on the famous day in Dublin in 1904 which is immortalized in Joyce's *Ulysses*; and, by a clever labyrinth (fig. 2), the visitor himself progressed through Joyce's life, personal and literary.

To a scholar the most important items were the many examples in small notebooks, normally used by French school children, of the first or second or third drafts of the various episodes of *Ulysses*. In addition, there were many notebooks illustrating the working habits of the author in preparing *Finnegans Wake*. The whole comprised one of the most striking exhibitions of the creative talent—in this case the talent of a genius—at work that anyone could be privileged to see.

The collection had been gathered together by Paul Léon and Eugène Jolas, friends of James Joyce when he lived in Paris—where he lived most of his working life. The two men had died, Léon at the hands of the Germans in a concentration camp. Their widows survived; Madame Léon was writing under the name of Lucie Noël for the *Paris Herald Tribune*; and Madame Jolas (fig. 3) was continuing her distinguished work as editor, translator, and author.[1]

By chance, I met Madame Léon, who kindly took me again to see the collection and greatly illuminated it for me by her perceptive and personal comments. I spoke to Monsieur Gheerbrant, the proprietor of the bookstore, about the ultimate disposal of the material. I had no thoughts that it might end up in Buffalo at that time, for we had no particular interest in Joyce beyond that of all literary people who were aware of the work of genius that *Ulysses* is. Gheerbrant said that the collection would be sold; but first it was to be exhibited in London.[2]

On my return home I talked with Mr. Ansley Sawyer and mentioned my impressions of the collection. Mr. and Mrs. Sawyer saw the exhibition in

(opposite page)
Joyce family portraits as exhibited in the Librairie La Hune's *Exposition en Hommage à James Joyce*, Paris, 1949.

*In 1949, Oscar A. Silverman was a professor of English at the University of Buffalo. He later served as both the chairman of the English Department (1956-1963) and director of the University Libraries (1960-1968). This article was first published as "James Joyce: Paris-Buffalo, The Joyce Collections at the Lockwood Memorial Library," *Grosvenor Society Occasional Papers* 1, no. 1 (Feb. 1964): 1-5, by the Grosvenor Society, Friends of the Buffalo and Erie County Public Library. It was later reprinted with the above title in *James Joyce, 1882-1941, Ulysses: 1922-1982: A Centenary Exhibition* (Buffalo: The Poetry/Rare Books Collection, 1982), [33-36], with annotations by Melissa Banta. The latter version appears here with a few slight changes.

1. Additional information about the saving and preserving of Joyce's books and personal effects is given by Lucie Léon in letters to O. A. Silverman, 22 and 23 June 1967, at Buffalo. Maria Jolas elaborates with further details about these events in a letter to Melissa Banta, 12 November 1973, at Buffalo, and in a conversation in Paris, May 1979. These letters are part of XVI: Other Correspondents in the James Joyce Collection.

2. See Gheerbrant, ed., *James Joyce: sa vie, son oeuvre, son rayonnement*. A catalogue of a twenty-fifth-year exhibition, *James Joyce et Paris*, Paris, 16-20 June, 1975, is also edited by Gheerbrant.

Fig. 1 Bloomsday map from Librairie La Hune's
Exposition en Hommage à James Joyce, Paris, 1949.

Fig. 2 Exhibition detail from Librairie La Hune's
Exposition en Hommage à James Joyce, Paris, 1949.

Fig. 3 Maria Jolas, May 1979.

Fig. 4 Charles D. Abbott (1900–1961). A professor of English and the first director of the University Libraries, Abbott founded the Poetry Collection in 1937.

3. In a conversation with Melissa Banta, on 20 September 1975 in Paris, Maria Jolas elaborates in some detail her meeting with Mr. and Mrs. Sawyer at the Librairie La Hune in the spring of 1950. See also the *Buffalo Evening News*, 3 August 1950.

the spring of 1950, where they met Madame Jolas, and returned to Buffalo enthusiastic about it.³ He it was who stimulated the late Mr. Charles Abbott (fig. 4), director of Libraries, and me further to look into the possibility of getting the collection for Buffalo.

One day early in the summer of 1950, a letter came from Monsieur Gheerbrant offering the collection to us. Presumably a similar letter went to several other libraries. Mr. Abbott telephoned me, and together we went over the catalogue which I had brought back from Paris. Both of us recognized immediately that what we saw was a magnificent opportunity to build up our own library.

An immediate telephone call to the late Chancellor Capen set him on the way to discussing the matter with the General Administration Committee of

Fig. 5 Sylvia Beach in her Paris apartment, circa 1959.

(opposite page)
Fig. 6 James Joyce and Sylvia Beach outside Shakespeare and Company, 1921.

4. See Slatin, "The Philip J. Wickser Collection." This collection includes approximately 600 items, outstanding among these are: the various holograph notebooks for *Finnegans Wake*; one manuscript volume of 1,017 pages, later published as *James Joyce's Scribbledehobble: The Ur-Workbook for "Finnegans Wake"*; eleven manuscripts of seven episodes of *Ulysses*; the first manuscript of *Exiles*; a manuscript of twenty-two epiphanies; three manuscripts of *Pomes Penyeach*; various other miscellaneous manuscripts; many holograph letters; Joyce's personal library of 468 items, including a wide variety of inscribed presentation copies; a comprehensive collection of his printed works in various editions; and in addition many personal effects, ranging from a collection of family portraits and photographs, to his cane and his glasses.

5. Connolly, *The Personal Library of James Joyce* and *James Joyce's Scribbledehobble: The Ur-Workbook for "Finnegans Wake"*; Joyce, *Epiphanies*. More recent publications include Mark Shechner's *Joyce in Nighttown* and contributions by Leslie Fiedler, Michael Groden, Margot Norris, and others. The collections have been used by scholars of both national and international stature.

the Council of the University. They were willing to underwrite the project if the librarian would attempt from private sources to secure the money. So that afternoon an option was cabled, an option drawn up by Mr. Louis Jaffee, Dean of the Law School. And partly because of our speed, partly because the chief competing library had recently spent a great deal of money on another collection, we to our great pleasure received the collection from Librairie La Hune.[4]

Next came the generous gesture on the part of Margaretta (Mrs. Philip J.) Wickser and her family, who contributed the amount necessary as a memorial to the late Philip J. Wickser, who had died in the summer of 1949. Mr. Wickser was a well known book collector in Buffalo as well as being a patron of the fine arts. A great gentleman, a man who loved the art of living, a stimulating conversationalist, and a good friend, the association of his name with the collection has been a continued source of pleasure to all of us who had known him.

A number of publications almost immediately issued from our collection. Early came, in the University of Buffalo Studies, an annotated listing prepared by Professor Thomas E. Connolly, of the books in the library of James Joyce which are a part of the collection.[5] Many scholars came to the library to use the materials: among them Professor Harry Levin of Harvard, Professor Richard Ellmann of Northwestern, and Professor Joseph Prescott of Wayne.

In 1958 through a series of circumstances, some of which are either too comic or too difficult for verification to detail here, we discovered that another collection of Joyce materials, that of Sylvia Beach (fig. 5), might be available. Miss Beach was the original publisher of *Ulysses* in 1922, when all other publishers felt that the risk was too great to take. Miss Beach ran a bookstore, "Shakespeare and Company" (fig. 6), on the rue de l'Odéon, on

Fig. 10 B. W. Huebsch.

6. *Les années vingt. Les écrivains américains à Paris et leurs amis, 1920-1930.* Some items in the Sylvia Beach collection are described in her *Catalogue of a Collection Containing Manuscripts and Rare Editions of James Joyce, a Few Manuscripts of Walt Whitman, and Two Drawings by William Blake, Belonging to Miss Sylvia Beach and Offered for Sale at Her Shop* (Paris: Shakespeare and Company, [1935]). See also *Paris in the Twenties*, the catalogue of an exhibition at U.S.I.S. Gallery, London, 1960.

7. See Townsend, "The Sylvia Beach Collection." This collection includes: the letters published in this volume, and considerable other correspondence relating to Joyce's activities, friendships, and publications; numerous materials about the composition and publication of *Ulysses*; a number of early manuscript drafts of episodes of *Ulysses*; over 1,200 pages in typescript with manuscript corrections; approximately 800 page proofs with corrections; many inscribed presentation copies, including copy no. 2 of *Ulysses*; variant printings, and translations of Joyce's work into several languages; copies of the two recordings of Joyce reading from *Ulysses* and *Finnegans Wake*; many photographs of Joyce and his family, supplementing those in the Wickser collection; and innumerable notations by Sylvia Beach identifying the several thousand items in the collection.

8. Included in the James Joyce Collection are letters, proofs, and errata sheets of *A Portrait of the Artist* given in 1951 and 1959 by the late B. W. Huebsch.

the left bank in Paris. An account of the bookstore and her life is given in her most entertaining and conversational—her tone of voice comes through—book called *Shakespeare and Company*.

Two young people in Buffalo, Dr. and Mrs. Walter F. Stafford, Jr., who were personal friends of mine, became excited at the possibility of getting the Beach collection for the University. A hasty trip was arranged; and the Saturday after Thanksgiving, the first week of jet service to Europe, three of us descended on Paris. Miss Beach really did not want us to come; she was busy preparing an exhibition to be opened in March 1959, by the Centre Culturel Américain. The exhibition was called "Les Années Vingt. Les Écrivains Américains à Paris et Leurs Amis, 1920-1930" and, of course, included Joyce, friend to many Americans.[6]

Miss Beach had insisted on the transatlantic telephone the previous week that she had no time to discuss the matter of disposing of her collection with us. Nevertheless, through the charm of the young woman, Mrs. Stafford, who, with her husband, was to present the collection to the University, Miss Beach agreed at least that she would make no disposition of her materials without giving us first chance.

A long series of letters followed. Increasingly it became clear that to Miss Beach the giving up of this material would be an emotional wrench which she found hard to contemplate. Finally details were arranged, and in the next summer, at Miss Beach's insistence, we returned to Paris to sort and to pack and to transport the treasures to Buffalo (figs. 7, 8, 9). She asked that they go by ship and that they be accompanied by one of us. I was delegated this pleasant task, and by September the Sylvia Beach collection had been added to the Wickser Collection in the Lockwood Memorial Library.[7]

In the meantime B. W. Huebsch (fig. 10), who had been Joyce's first publisher in the United States, had made a contribution to the Library of a number of important documents about Joyce as well as several manuscripts.[8]

By now the Library had one of the great Joyce collections in the world. Cornell, to be sure, through its purchase of the collection made by James' brother Stanislaus, had far more family papers. The Lockwood Library (now the Poetry/Rare Books Collection at Buffalo) had the bulk of the literary material except for the manuscript of *Finnegans Wake*, which is in the British Museum, the corrected manuscript of *Ulysses*, which is still held by the Rosenbach Foundation, and important and valuable materials at Yale and Harvard and other universities.

In 1962 Sylvia Beach died suddenly. The residue of her Joyce collection was offered to us for first refusal. The same two people, Dr. and Mrs. Stafford, who had purchased the original Sylvia Beach collection generously contributed the major part of the amount necessary to buy the rest of the Beach collection.

Figs. 7, 8, 9 Scenes from Sylvia Beach's apartment in Paris.

(opposite page)
Oscar A. Silverman in Paris.

9. See Cotton, "The Poetry Collection of the Lockwood Memorial Library"; Alvarez, "A Library of Poetry"; Abbott, "The Poet's Workshop" and introduction to *Poets at Work*.

Complementing this gift was one from Mrs. Spencer Kittinger which, added to an allocation from the Friends of the Lockwood Memorial Library, made the purchase possible.

Before we received the final shipment of the Beach collection, Dr. Peter Spielberg published his catalogue *James Joyce's Manuscripts and Letters at the University of Buffalo*, an annotated index to all of the materials then available. Mr. Spielberg worked for several years on this catalogue; it is still a primary source to the many Joyce scholars throughout this country and abroad.

The Joyce collections (as well as the magnificent collection of twentieth-century poetry in English, books, manuscripts, letters, and worksheets in the Lockwood Memorial Library) are available to all qualified scholars.[9] Much of the material has been photographed on microfilm, which is sent on interlibrary loan all over the world to students of Joyce.

A list of those who have acknowledged their debt to the Lockwood Memorial Library's collection of Joyce would be much too long for the compass of this article. Happily, the name of Buffalo and its university has become better known throughout the scholarly world. More important, we have had the privilege of contributing in small measure to the scholarship interpreting, defining, and appreciating one of the greatest writers of the twentieth century.

WORKS CITED

Alvarez, A. "A Library of Poetry." *The Listener* 60, no. 1531 (31 July 1958): 155-56.

Abbott, Charles. D. Introduction to *Poets at Work*, 1-36. New York: Harcourt, Brace, 1948.

———. "The Poet's Workshop." *The Saturday Review of Literature* 25, no. 17 (25 April 1942): 10-11, 14.

Catalogue of a Collection Containing Manuscripts and Rare Editions of James Joyce, a Few Manuscripts of Walt Whitman, and Two Drawings by William Blake, Belonging to Miss Sylvia Beach and Offered for Sale at Her Shop. Paris: Shakespeare and Company, [1935].

Centre Culturel Américain. *Les années vingt. Les écrivains américains à Paris et leurs amis, 1920-1930.* Paris: Les Presses Artistiques, [1959].

Connolly, Thomas E., ed. *James Joyce's Scribbledehobble: The Ur-Workbook for "Finnegans Wake."* Evanston, IL: Northwestern University Press, 1961.

Connolly, Thomas E. *The Personal Library of James Joyce: A Descriptive Bibliography. The University of Buffalo Studies.* Vol. 22, no. 1. Buffalo: University of Buffalo, 1955.

Cotton, John. "The Poetry Collection of the Lockwood Memorial Library." *Private Library* 8, no. 4 (Winter 1975): 149-53.

Gheerbrant, Bernard, ed. *James Joyce et Paris.* Paris: Bibliothèque publique d'information, 1975.

———. *James Joyce: sa vie, son oeuvre, son rayonnement.* Paris: La Hune, 1949.

Joyce, James. *Epiphanies.* Introduction and notes by Oscar A. Silverman. Buffalo: Lockwood Memorial Library, University of Buffalo, 1956.

XVI: Other Correspondents. PCMS-020. James Joyce Collection. 1900-1959. The Poetry Collection, The State University of New York at Buffalo.

Paris in the Twenties: An Exhibition of Souvenirs of British, French and American Writers, from Shakespeare and Company. London: USIS Gallery, 1960.

Shechner, Mark. *Joyce in Nighttown: A Psychoanalytic Inquiry into "Ulysses."* Berkeley: University of California Press, 1974.

Slatin, Myles. "The Philip J. Wickser Collection." In "Joyce Comes to Rest in Lockwood Library." *The University of Buffalo Alumni Bulletin* 27, no. 1 (March 1960): 7.

Spielberg, Peter, comp. *James Joyce's Manuscripts and Letters at the University of Buffalo: A Catalogue.* Buffalo: University of Buffalo, 1962.

Townsend, J. Benjamin. "The Sylvia Beach Collection." In "Joyce Comes to Rest in Lockwood Library." *The University of Buffalo Alumni Bulletin* 27, no. 1 (March 1960): 8-10.

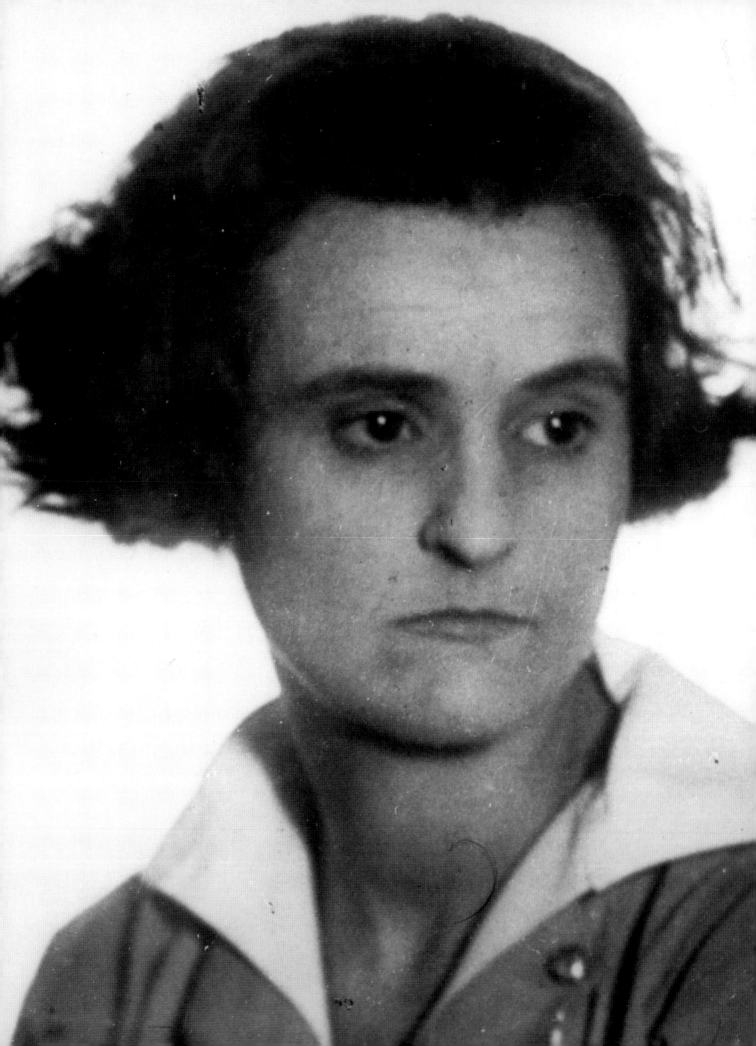

SYLVIA BEACH'S JOYCE COLLECTION AT BUFFALO

Luca Crispi

Sylvia Beach's links with Buffalo began in 1949 in Paris when she, Maria Jolas, and Lucie Léon toured Oscar Silverman, then a professor in the English department, around the Librairie La Hune's James Joyce Exhibition. This collection was purchased the following year with a donation that Margaretta F. Wickser had given to the Lockwood Memorial Library in memory of her husband, Philip J. Wickser, one of Buffalo's great book collectors. But Beach's personal association with Buffalo was cemented ten years later when Constance and Walter F. Stafford traveled to Paris to visit her at Shakespeare and Company. The friendship that arose between them ensured that Beach's own collection would join Joyce's in the Poetry Collection. Since then the Wickser, Banta, Stafford, and Constantine families' enduring enthusiasm and generosity have continued to promote Joyce-related scholarship and cultural events in Buffalo.

In 1959, after her only visit to Buffalo, Sylvia Beach wrote to Charles Abbott, the director of Libraries, to say that she "felt immensely privileged to be escorted through your magnificent library [...] and to be shown some of your most precious, carefully-guarded treasures. Naturally, it was your James Joyce collection that interested me particularly, and it was indeed a great joy to see how admirably you have arranged the memorial to him there. I am very glad to think that Joycean scholars and Joyce-lovers will always flock to the [...] Library in Buffalo."[1] With this exhibition and conference exactly fifty years later, Beach's prediction continues to be proven true.

While many of the headlines in the Joyce world since 2000 have been filled with accounts of the astounding number of newly discovered Joyce manuscripts and related material—and rightly so—the largest and most comprehensive Joyce archive in the world is still in the University at Buffalo's Poetry Collection. Almost half of the manuscripts reproduced in the pioneering *James Joyce Archive* are actually in Buffalo and most of them were Sylvia Beach's, including ten of the twenty drafts of *Ulysses* as well as *all* of its typescripts and proofs. Without her collection of manuscripts, it would not have been possible to reconstruct how Joyce wrote *Ulysses*.

Like Harriet Shaw Weaver, Sylvia Beach also became Joyce's publisher and then his archivist, but unlike the meticulous Englishwoman, Beach had her own way of approaching these endeavors. Almost two years after the main

(opposite page)
Sylvia Beach, Paris, circa 1922.

1. XII: Correspondence from Sylvia Beach: Sylvia Beach to Charles Abbott; 17 June 1959, unpublished.

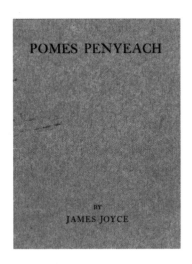

Fig. 11 *Pomes Penyeach* (Paris: Shakespeare and Company, 1927).

Fig. 12 *Our Exagmination Round His Factification for Incamination of Work in Progress* (Paris: Shakespeare and Company, 1929).

2. XII: Sylvia Beach to Oscar Silverman no. 19; undated [probably late 1961 to early 1962], unpublished.

3. XIII: Correspondence to Sylvia Beach and Shakespeare and Company: Richard Aldington to Sylvia Beach; 5 December 1929, unpublished.

consignment of her Joyce collection arrived in Buffalo, Beach sent a guileless letter to Silverman. It shows how she had come to feel at home with her Joyceana over the years:

> In turning out my cupboard I have come across some typescript pages of ULYSSES: [...] of which about 168 were numbered by Joyce and a few contain his corrections: [...] I will send them by registered mail if you want them: also, [...] a bundle of 'placards' with the earliest dates from the printinghouse[.] There are about 179 of these 'placards['] of the 1st edition of ULYSSES but they contain no corrections and only go from Part I to the "Wandering Rocks" so are not even complete as a set of proofs. They are hardly worth any bother. They can be kept with other souvenirs of Shakespeare and Company's activities. [...]
>
> P.S. The typescript pages are not consecutive but mixed up as Joyce left them and might fit in with yours somewhere.[2]

But the historical and scholarly value of Beach's Joyce collection is greater than the thousands of manuscript pages it contains and until recently the scope and depth of this material were not widely known. Making this part of its Joyce Collection available will further establish Buffalo as a center for "Joycean scholars and Joyce-lovers."

I still vividly remember the excitement and bewilderment I felt when Michael Basinski, the Poetry Collection's present curator, first showed me a dozen or so banker's boxes that were all generically labeled "Shakespeare and Company Business Correspondence." It soon became clear that Shakespeare and Company's "business" was to publish and sell Joyce's works. There are hundreds of letters here that deal with its publications of *Ulysses* and *Pomes Penyeach* (fig. 11) as well as *Our Exagmination Round His Factification for Incamination of Work in Progress* (fig. 12). Since Shakespeare and Company was the Paris hub of literary modernism, the boxes were filled with requests from bibliophiles and booksellers around the world, not just the Poetry Bookshop in London or the Sunwise Turn or the Washington Square bookshops in New York City, but also from customers from Ireland to India and so many places in between.

For over fifteen years, Shakespeare and Company was the surest way of reaching Joyce, and so Richard Aldington wrote directly to Beach: "I enclose herewith a cheque for four pounds, Mr Joyce's share of the advance on the American edition of the Imagist Anthology. I am sending it to you because I am not quite sure of his address."[3] Everyone turned to her for assistance, including Maggs Bros. in Paris who wrote, "One of our clients has asked us

First edition of *Ulysses* (Paris: Shakespeare and Company, 1922).

to secure for him a specimen autograph-letter signed by James Joyce, and it has occurred to us that you would be the best able to supply this. Perhaps you could let us know if you can do so and at what price."[4]

Questions about the material production and dissemination of Shakespeare and Company's first edition of *Ulysses* have been of interest not just to bibliographers and textual scholars. The work's physical design, printing, and especially the stories about its sales have prompted heated critical and cultural debates. Unfortunately, the same supposed "facts" have been recounted so many times, usually based on inaccurate personal anecdotes, that these stories have by now entered the realm of myth. Hopefully, Beach's archival material in Buffalo will now prompt a corrected and more complete history of the work's status as one of the principal gauges of the commercial forces of modernism.

4. XIII: Maggs Bros. to Shakespeare and Company; 6 October 1928, unpublished.

The 157 letters from the Imprimerie Darantiere to Shakespeare and Company from 28 July 1920 (when they had printed 3,000 copies of the lending library's iconic bookplate) to 20 October 1931 (six months after they had printed the "eleventh" and last Shakespeare and Company impression of *Ulysses*) are replete with practical and textual details as well as unexpected financial issues that will certainly alter our understanding of the book's production.[5] On 16 June 1921—no less—shortly after the first proofs had been set, Maurice Darantiere, head of the printing house in Dijon, made the first of his many pleas to Joyce to return the corrected copies in a timely fashion so that the printing could continue. Neither Darantiere nor Beach knew that Joyce had still to finish writing the last two episodes of the book. In fact, Joyce himself could not have known how difficult writing those 113 pages—a full one-sixth of the book as published—would prove to be. Darantiere also reminded Beach that, as agreed, any additions the author made on the proofs would incur a further charge. By 3 December 1921, the bill for Joyce's additions and changes was already 3,852 francs. Ultimately, they would account for almost a quarter of the entire printing costs of the first edition of *Ulysses!*

One of the many archival treasures for material modernist scholarship in Buffalo is an address book Beach kept in the crucial period from 1921 to 1922. Among sundry Shakespeare and Company business, it was Beach's original accounting diary for *Ulysses*.[6] Although incomplete and not fully

James Joyce with Sylvia Beach at Shakespeare and Company, 1922.

5. Based on earlier work by Sam Slote, Erika Ledermann has recently prepared a summary-translation of this correspondence. Although Beach's letters to Darantiere are no longer extant, there are two of Beach's letters to Baron Bernard d'Avout at the firm. In the last one Beach comments on the lifting of the ban in the United States and says she is sorry to say that their collaboration in the publication of this book, which has lasted so many years, is over (see XIII: d'Avout to Beach; 15 February 1934, unpublished).

6. Beach transcribed the data from this accounting diary to another notebook, which is now in the Harry Ransom Humanities Research Center at the University of Texas at Austin. See Barnes, "Sylvia Beach's *Ulysses* Notebook: Census of the 100 Series."

reliable, it is nonetheless a primary source of information about the trade in *Ulysses*.[7] Inside the front cover, Beach recorded the memorable fact that the first two copies of the book arrived by train on 2 February 1922, the very day *Ulysses* was published. The first entry under "J" correspondingly notes Joyce's birth date. Day by day, Beach also kept track of some of the replies to the subscription notices she received and later logged when the books were finally paid for (often in installments) and then distributed. Unsurprisingly, the entries under "J" prove to be the most interesting of all. They comprise an eccentric accounting of the various loans Beach made to Joyce beginning on 12 July 1921. In mid-November Beach had filled "J" and the accounts spill over to "K." The reckoning continues on to "L" after *Ulysses* had appeared, and we see the same pattern of further loans and partial repayments throughout. This accounting ends a year after it was started on 17 July 1922 with Joyce's debt still outstanding.[8] Ten days later, Beach typed up a "ULYSSES / Account Rendered" memorandum that, among other things, states that the printing of *Ulysses* cost 42,492 francs (twice as much as had originally been estimated on 25 April 1921) and postage so far had cost 3,200 francs. By then 39,505 francs had been "paid to Mr. James Joyce," which is almost 30% of the net receipts of the book's sales from 19 May 1921 to 27 July 1922, whereas Beach had only received 13,978.80, or just about 10%.[9] All told, these documents are some of the most fundamental records of the material and financial aspects of the production of modernism's most prized work.[10]

7. Seventy-five filled-in *Ulysses* subscription forms are also part of the Buffalo Joyce Collection; the remaining forms are in the Beach and Shakespeare and Company archive in the Department of Rare Books and Special Collections, Firestone Library, Princeton University. See http://arks.princeton.edu/ark:/88435/7h149p866.

8. XX: Miscellaneous Sylvia Beach and Shakespeare and Company Material, folder 5. As far as I can ascertain the accounts never tally up and in many ways remind us of Joyce's own attempts to forge his accounts in the "Paris and Pola Commonplace Book," the original of which recently reappeared and is National Library of Ireland MS 36,639/02/A.

9. XVIII: Miscellaneous Material Related to Joyce's Works, E.I, folder 21. It seems Beach followed Joyce's example; her accounting diary also records her own loans from her mother and from Adrienne Monnier.

10. Given all the practical and financial problems Beach had with her first edition, it is interesting she would tell Ernest Boyd in October 1922 that "I am sure you will be glad to hear that the first edition of 'Ulysses' went off so well. In fact copies are now being sold in London for forty pounds. The second edition of two thousand copies was almost completely subscribed when it appeared last week" (XII: Beach to Boyd; undated, unpublished).

Shakespeare and Company business card.

Much of Beach's correspondence documents her negotiations with a steady stream of French (fig. 13), Czech, Polish, German (fig. 14), and even two competing Japanese translators as well as composers who wanted to set Joyce's poems to music and publishers of new editions of Joyce's earlier works. Even with sympathetic publishers, the problems Joyce experienced with his earliest printers continued to plague him. In 1924, just as the first fragments of the French translation of *Ulysses* were appearing in Adrienne Monnier's magazine *Commerce*, Jonathan Cape took over the English publication of *A Portrait of the Artist as a Young Man* (fig. 15). As he was resetting the type, Cape wrote to Beach:

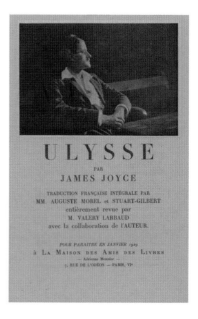

Fig. 13 Advertisement for the French translation of *Ulysses*.

> [...] our printer has departed from his copy [of the Egoist Press edition] as he does not agree with the way it has been done. The previous printers were an odd sort of firm who are not used to book work and I have no doubt that our printer is right in most of the corrections he has made. I fear however that he may have corrected things which Mr. Joyce particularly wishes to be rendered in a certain way. For instance my printer puts 'Oh' where Mr. Joyce may use a single 'O'.
>
> It would seem that as we are setting the book up and shall get it into permanent form we ought to get it corrected in conformity with Mr. Joyce's ideas. As you are closely in touch with him I am sending you a set of proofs together with the original copy. Would you mind asking him to correct it, or if he is unable to do it himself (it may be a trouble as I believe his eyesight fails him) he could no doubt depute the work to someone.[11]

Joyce was away at the time and Beach's response is not in the Buffalo Collection, but we have Cape's reply to her instructions less than a week later:

> While there is no justification for the printers having altered some of the punctuation, spelling and so forth, I do think that there is something to be said for the use of single quotation marks instead of dashes to indicate quoted matter. If I undertake to have all of Mr Joyce's punctuation and spelling altered so that it is exactly as printed in the original edition, do you think that he will allow us to retain the quotation marks instead of the dashes which were used in the previous edition? I find, and others agree with me, that when dashes are used the book is far more difficult to read, and while quotation marks are not an ideal way of expressing speech, single ones do not obtrude themselves unnecessarily, and in fact are less obvious and unsightly than those long dashes.[12]

Fig. 14 Georg Goyert, German translator of *Ulysses*, 1927.

11. XIII: Jonathan Cape to Sylvia Beach; 27 June 1924, unpublished.

12. XIII: G. Wren Howard [for Cape] to Sylvia Beach; 2 July 1924, unpublished.

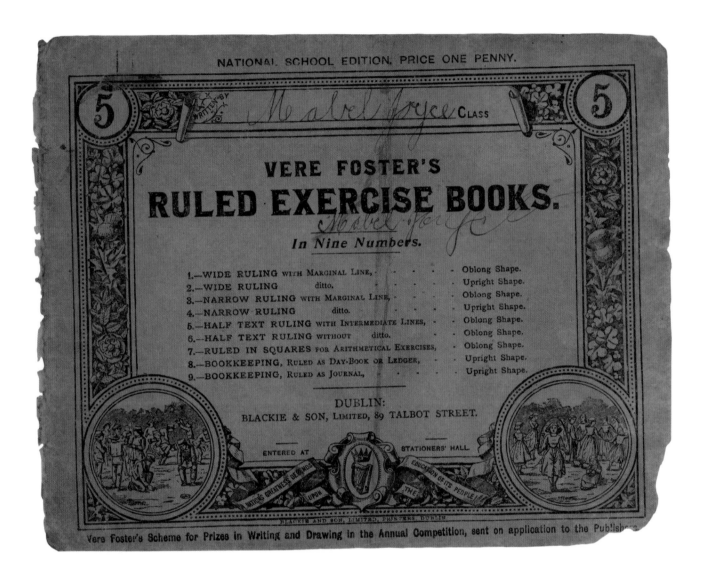

Fig. 15 This 1904 notebook contains Joyce's "A Portrait of the Artist" essay, the semi-autobiographical sketch of what would later evolve into *A Portrait of the Artist as a Young Man*. The essay was written in Mabel Joyce's Vere Foster's exercise book. Mabel was Joyce's sister (1893–1911). In 1928 Joyce gave the notebook to Sylvia Beach.

Joyce's view on the use of quotation marks of any kind, which he called "perverted commas," was always clear and firm, and the Cape edition appeared as Joyce had wanted it.

Acting on Joyce's behalf, Beach was also concerned with the publication of his new works, first in the little magazine *transition* in Paris and then the deluxe editions of *Anna Livia Plurabelle* (New York: Crosby Gaige, 1928), *Tales Told of Shem and Shaun* (Paris: Black Sun Press, 1929), *Haveth Childers Everywhere* (New York: Fountain Press, 1930) (fig. 16), and *The Mime of Mick, Nick and the Maggies* (The Hague: Servire Press, 1934) (fig. 17) as well as *Haveth Childers Everywhere* and *Two Tales of Shem and Shaun* (London: Faber and Faber, 1931 and 1932). Besides looking out for Joyce's financial interests, Beach kept track of his manuscripts as they traveled back and forth to the various printers of his *Work in Progress*, especially when he was away from Paris. As with *Ulysses*, Joyce constantly made additions and changes to his texts and often recorded them in his letters to Beach as well as on all manner of scraps of paper that Beach preserved in her business correspondence files. Even these miscellaneous manuscripts expand our understanding of the care with which Joyce crafted all of his texts.

Also of interest in the collection of correspondence are the contentious exchanges with publishing pirates, like the infamous Samuel Roth and Jacob Schwartz, and the less well-known but just as disingenuous booklegger Alexander H. Buchman, all of whom were taking advantage of conflicting copyright issues and profiting from Joyce's works and fame. Besides the countless letters from critics around the world who asked for further information and guidance about his works or for news about Joyce, there are also letters from his faithful readers and enthusiasts, such as DeWitt Eldridge of the University of Virginia:

NEWS FLASH.

The Pope has blessed Ulysses.

I bought a copy of Mr. Joyce's *Ulysses* at your shop and took it to Italy with me. I was granted an interview with the Pope; and when His Holiness blessed my prayer-book which I extended to him, he also blessed a copy of *Ulysses* which I had conceiled [sic] beneath it.

It may cheer Mr. Joyce to know that whatever treatment *Ulysses* may have had in America, in Vatican City it was blessed.

A reader of *Ulysses* whose admiration for Mr. Joyce could not be contained in a letter[.][13]

As well as letters from a long list of now famous writers and artists who were Beach's friends and counted on her in so many ways, over time, there were letters from journalists who were just as interested in telling the story of Sylvia

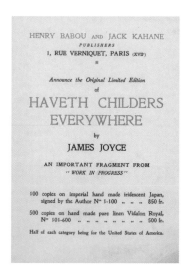

Fig. 16 Announcement for the Paris version of the 1930 Fountain Press edition of *Haveth Childers Everywhere*.

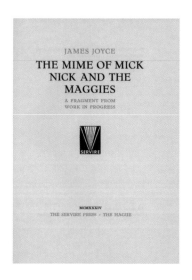

Fig. 17 Title page from *The Mime of Mick, Nick and the Maggies* (The Hague: Servire Press, 1934).

13. XIII: DeWitt Eldridge to Sylvia Beach; 18 September 1933, unpublished.

Beach, the adventurous daughter of a Presbyterian minister from Princeton, New Jersey, whose bookshop had become a center of the contemporary literary scene in Paris. Buffalo's Joyce Collection preserves a magnificent abundance of research material about James Joyce and Sylvia Beach, as well as the writers and patrons who frequented Shakespeare and Company. As Beach predicted, it will continue to foster a wide range of literary historical studies, exhibitions and gatherings such as this.

Pictured here with University Council President Seymour H. Knox (left) and other honorary degree recipients, Sylvia Beach was awarded an honorary doctorate from the University of Buffalo in June, 1959. Beach was honored as "An American citizen wearing the French Legion of Honor.... Courageous and far-seeing, Miss Beach published the original edition of James Joyce's *Ulysses* when no other publisher dared bring out this great book."

WORKS CITED

Barnes, Laura. "Sylvia Beach's *Ulysses* Notebook: Census of the 100 Series." In *James Joyce: Books and Manuscripts*, 109-34. New York: Glenn Horowitz Bookseller, 1996.

XII: Correspondence from Sylvia Beach. PCMS-020. James Joyce Collection. 1900-1959. The Poetry Collection, The State University of New York at Buffalo.

XIII: Correspondence to Sylvia Beach and Shakespeare and Company. PCMS-020. James Joyce Collection. 1900-1959. The Poetry Collection, The State University of New York at Buffalo.

XVIII: Miscellaneous Material Related to Joyce's Works. PCMS-020. James Joyce Collection. 1900-1959. The Poetry Collection, The State University of New York at Buffalo.

XX: Miscellaneous Sylvia Beach and Shakespeare and Company Material. PCMS-020. James Joyce Collection. 1900-1959. The Poetry Collection, The State University of New York at Buffalo.

Joyce family coat of arms
No date
Paint and ink on paper
14 ¾ x 11

JOYCE FAMILY PORTRAIT GALLERY

Among the items acquired by Buffalo from the Librairie La Hune's *Exposition en Hommage à James Joyce* were Joyce's family portraits, the Joyce family crest, and the Joyce family coat of arms. Joyce attributed the paintings of his grandparents to John Comerford of Cork. However, John Comerford was a painter of miniatures. It is possible that Joyce's father acquired the portraits in an effort to boost the Joyce family's social status.

Renowned Irish painter Patrick Tuohy was born in Dublin in 1894. When Tuohy painted Joyce in Paris in 1924 it took him twenty-eight sittings. Joyce later included Tuohy in *Finnegans Wake*, referring to him as "Ratatuohy."

Professor James Hamm of Buffalo State College's Art Conservation Department and his students stabilized, cleaned, and conserved the Joyce family oils during the summer of 2008.

Patrick Tuohy (Irish, 1894–1930)
James Joyce, circa 1924
Oil on canvas
24 x 19 ¾

John Comerford (Irish, flourished 1800s), *attrib. by James Joyce*
Anne McCann Joyce, circa 1845
Joyce's paternal great-grandmother
Oil on canvas
30 ¼ x 25

John Comerford (Irish, flourished 1800s), *attrib. by James Joyce*
James Joyce (1800–1855?), circa 1845
Joyce's paternal great-grandfather
Oil on canvas
30 x 25

John Comerford (Irish, flourished 1800s), *attrib. by James Joyce*
Ellen O'Connell Joyce (1816–1881), circa 1845
Joyce's paternal grandmother
Oil on canvas
30 x 25

John Comerford (Irish, flourished 1800s), *attrib. by James Joyce*
James Augustine Joyce (1827–1866), circa 1845
Joyce's paternal grandfather, as a young man
Oil on canvas
25 ½ x 19

John Comerford (Irish, flourished 1800s), *attrib. by James Joyce*
James Augustine Joyce (1827–1866), circa 1855
Joyce's paternal grandfather
Oil on canvas
30 x 25

Patrick Tuohy (Irish, 1894–1930)
John Stanislaus Joyce (1849–1931), circa 1924
Joyce's father
Oil on canvas
39 ½ x 32

Patrick Tuohy (Irish, 1894–1930)
Mary Joyce (1859–1903), 1926
Joyce's mother, drawn from a photograph dated 1888 (page 77)
Pencil on paper
16 ½ x 12 ⅝

Patrick Tuohy (Irish, 1894–1930)
Lucia Joyce (1907–1982), 1927
Joyce's daughter
Pencil on paper
15 x 12

Tullio Silvestri (Italian, 1880–1963)
Nora Barnacle Joyce, 1914
Joyce's wife
Oil on burlap
35 ½ x 29 ½

Tullio Silvestri (Italian, 1880–1963)
James Joyce, 1914
Watercolor on paper
19 ¼ x 15 ⅛

Constantin Brancusi (Romanian, 1876-1957)
James Joyce, 1929
Pencil on paper
8 ¼ x 6 ¼

Frank Budgen (British, 1882–1971)
Nora Barnacle Joyce, circa 1919
Joyce's wife
Oil on paperboard
22 ⅛ x 17 ⅝

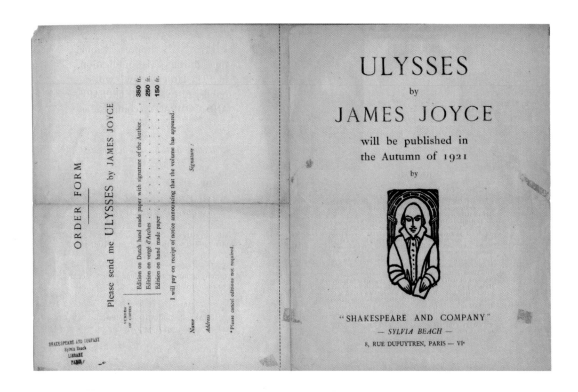

ORDER FORM

Please send me ULYSSES by JAMES JOYCE

NUMBER OF COPIES

Édition on Dutch hand made paper with signature of the Author . . . . **350** fr.
Édition on vergé d'Arches . . . . **250** fr.
Édition on hand made paper . . . . **150** fr.

I will pay on receipt of notice announcing that the volume has appeared.

Signature :

Name
Address
*Please cancel editions not required.

SHAKESPEARE AND COMPANY
Sylvia Beach
LIBRARY
PARIS

ULYSSES
by
JAMES JOYCE
will be published in
the Autumn of 1921
by

"SHAKESPEARE AND COMPANY"
— SYLVIA BEACH —
8, RUE DUPUYTREN, PARIS — VIᵉ

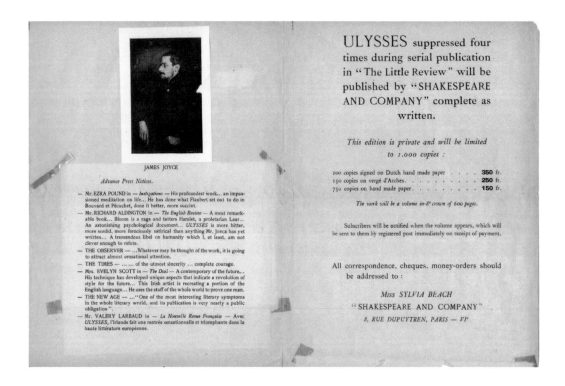

JAMES JOYCE

Advance Press Notices.

— Mr. EZRA POUND in — *Instigations* — His profoundest work... an impassioned meditation on life... He has done what Flaubert set out to do in Bouvard et Pécuchet, done it better, more succint.

— Mr. RICHARD ALDINGTON in — *The English Review* — A most remarkable book... Bloom is a rags and tatters Hamlet, a proletarian Lear... An astonishing psychological document... ULYSSES is more bitter, more sordid, more ferociously satirical than anything Mr. Joyce has yet written... A tremendous libel on humanity which I, at least, am not clever enough to refute.

— THE OBSERVER — ...Whatever may be thought of the work, it is going to attract almost sensational attention.

— THE TIMES — ... ... of the utmost sincerity ... complete courage.

— Mrs. EVELYN SCOTT in — *The Dial* — A contemporary of the future... His technique has developed unique aspects that indicate a revolution of style for the future... This Irish artist is recreating a portion of the English language... He uses the stuff of the whole world to prove one man.

— THE NEW AGE — ..."One of the most interesting literary symptoms in the whole literary world, and its publication is very nearly a public obligation".

— Mr. VALERY LARBAUD in — *La Nouvelle Revue Française* — Avec ULYSSES, l'Irlande fait une rentrée sensationnelle et triomphante dans la haute littérature européenne.

ULYSSES suppressed four times during serial publication in "The Little Review" will be published by "SHAKESPEARE AND COMPANY" complete as written.

This edition is private and will be limited to 1.000 copies :

100 copies signed on Dutch hand made paper . . . . **350** fr.
150 copies on vergé d'Arches . . . . **250** fr.
750 copies on hand made paper . . . . **150** fr.

The work will be a volume in-8° crown of 600 pages.

Subscribers will be notified when the volume appears, which will be sent to them by registered post immediately on receipt of payment.

All correspondence, cheques, money-orders should be addressed to :

Miss SYLVIA BEACH
"SHAKESPEARE AND COMPANY"
8, RUE DUPUYTREN, PARIS — VIᵉ

Early printing of Shakespeare and Company's prospectus with subscription form for *Ulysses*.

ON FIRST LOOKING INTO JAMES JOYCE'S MANUSCRIPTS

Michael Groden

I first encountered Joyce's manuscripts in summer 1973 as a desperate Princeton University graduate student. I had spent a year writing an unsuccessful doctoral dissertation chapter, and I needed to find an entirely new topic. My supervisor, A. Walton Litz, mentioned that many new Joyce documents had come to light since he had written *The Art of James Joyce*, his well-known but then twelve-year-old book on Joyce's manuscripts for *Ulysses* and *Finnegans Wake*. Maybe, he suggested, I could look at the newly available materials and augment or update his work.

The University at Buffalo possessed the largest new collection, assembled in the 1950s and early 1960s. According to Peter Spielberg's catalogue (fig. 18) from 1962, Buffalo owned many drafts of individual *Ulysses* episodes. I was startled to realize that these documents resided only a few blocks away from the suburban Buffalo house where I grew up.

I ordered two microfilm reels of *Ulysses* drafts from UB's Poetry Collection. Before they arrived, I looked at Phillip Herring's edition of the British Museum *Ulysses* notesheets, then less than a year old. Discouraged, I could not see any project developing from them. I became intrigued, though, whenever I encountered familiar words from *Ulysses*. One note, for instance, read "Inisfail the fair," part of a sentence from early in "Cyclops."[1] Another was "Jew: love his country when sure which it is (SD. P. M'H)"; the initials at the end puzzled me, but the rest echoed a vicious anti-Semitic exchange in the episode.[2] I also registered Herring's puzzlement over Joyce's use of red, blue, and green crayons. Joyce crossed out many notes with a crayon, and Herring found some of them, including "Inisfail" and "love his country," in the published *Ulysses*. He could not find many other intriguing "Cyclops" notes—"LB made up to mother-in-law" (a reference to Molly's mother?? Molly says in "Penelope" that she does not know who her mother was)[3] or a primitive four-line poem about Ireland—however, and no pattern at all emerged.

When the microfilms arrived, I sat at the dark, cumbersome reader and glanced at the page images. I marveled at Joyce's handwriting—there, in front of me!—and at the visually stunning pages. Sometimes Joyce wrote in ink, sometimes in pencil. His writing was small and often very difficult to read. When he used a copybook, he began writing on the rectos (right-hand pages),

1. Joyce, *Joyce's "Ulysses" Notesheets in the British Museum*, 115 ("Cyclops" notesheet 8:68), hereafter cited as *Notesheets*, followed by notesheet number:line number; Joyce, *The James Joyce Archive* 12:11, hereafter cited as *Archive*, followed by volume number:page number; see Joyce, *Ulysses: The Gabler Edition* 12:68, 241, hereafter cited as *Ulysses*, followed by episode number:line number and then page number.

2. *Notesheets*, 102 ("Cyclops" notesheet 5:76); *Archive* 12:7; see *Ulysses* 12:1628-30, 276.

3. *Notesheets*, 100 ("Cyclops" notesheet 5:1); *Archive* 12:7; *Ulysses* 18:846-47, 627.

Fig. 18 Peter Spielberg, comp., *James Joyce's Manuscripts and Letters at the University of Buffalo: A Catalogue* (Buffalo: University of Buffalo, 1962).

Fig. 19 These colored dashes, found in Joyce's personal copy of Thomas Moore's *Moore's Irish Melodies* (London; New York; Melbourne; Sydney: Ward, Lock, Bowden & Co., [between 1890 and 1896?]), resemble in color the pencil marks found throughout Joyce's notebooks.

with a left margin that widened as he moved down the page. To revise, he crossed out words and wrote new ones above or below them or nearby in a margin, often with a line connecting the body of the text to the marginal words. He added words, phrases, or longer passages above or below the line, in the margins (connected by a line or signaled by a superscript "F" or another letter), or on the facing verso page. Long additions are almost always on the versos, and sometimes they run over onto another page, with Joyce occasionally moving from the copybook's back towards the front. It can be unclear where a bit of marginal text fits into the main text, and sometimes the pages become so cluttered that following the lines connecting words in the body of the text with those in the margins becomes difficult or even impossible. Joyce obviously knew how all the elements fit together and did not need a precise visual indicator, but it astonished me that anyone could have known how the various bits of text on a page related to each other. Colored lines and Xs often cover full pages or sections of pages (fig. 19). In the black-and-white microfilms, the writing and markings all appeared as black and different shades of grey. Later, my first look at the original documents in the Poetry Collection resembled the sudden shift from black-and-white to color in *The Wizard of Oz*: the pages were tan, not white; Joyce wrote in various shades of ink and pencil; and the diagonal lines, Xs, and other markings appeared in Technicolor.

The British Museum notesheets cover only the last seven episodes, starting with "Cyclops," and so I began my reading with that episode's two drafts. I started with two reasonably clearly written large sheets containing four scenes and a fragment of a fifth which Spielberg in his catalogue designated as the earlier of the two drafts and numbered as V.A.6. I had trouble deciphering Joyce's handwriting, but I slowly became acclimated to his formation of letters, and aided by the published *Ulysses* I was able to make out many, though hardly all, of the words.

I was fascinated when I encountered early versions of scenes that differed greatly from their published forms and also scenes that Joyce had apparently discarded entirely as he developed the episode. One very different scene was a discussion of Ireland and Jews. Stephen Dedalus, nowhere in the published episode, not only hobnobs here with the bigoted men in the pub but also offers the anti-Semitic answer to the question about a Jew loving his country.[4] How could Joyce have included Stephen here, not only in a scene containing the most virulently anti-Semitic words that Leopold Bloom, the man who will rescue him a few hours later, is forced to hear during the day, but even speaking them himself? Also here is Professor MacHugh, who like Stephen appears earlier in "Aeolus," and so the initials "SD. P. M'H" in Joyce's note referred to these two characters. In a scene that Joyce discarded, the men gossip about Bloom and Molly, mentioning rumors that they are going to be divorced and that, to

4. Buffalo MS V.A.6, 2r; Joyce, *Joyce's Notes and Early Drafts for "Ulysses,"* 181, hereafter cited as *Notes*; *Archive* 13:134c.

James Joyce, bearded, three-quarter view, Zurich, 1919.

win Molly, Bloom "made {sucked} up to his mother-in-law."[5] Surprisingly, many of the characters are unnamed, with much of the dialogue attributed to a speaker identified only by a dash or an X (reversing the pattern, though, the published version's Citizen is named Cusack here); the hilariously vitriolic unnamed first-person narrator is largely undeveloped; and some of the writing is quite unformed compared to the published text, as in "Then did you speak, noble Cusack, lifting up your voice, and all men hearkened."[6]

The draft was gripping, but staring for hours into the dark microfilm reader and hearing the screechy grinding of the handcrank that I turned to move the film forwards and backwards were giving me a backache and headache. Near the end of the day, however, all physical discomfort evaporated as I unexpectedly experienced the first of two "Eureka!" moments regarding the "Cyclops" drafts. Following one scene, Joyce wrote a little poem:

5. Buffalo MS V.A.6, 2v; *Notes*, 182; *Archive* 13:134d.

6. Buffalo MS V.A.6, 1v; *Notes*, 179; *Archive* 13:134b.

O Ireland! Our sireland!

Once fireland! Now mireland!

No liar land shall buy our land!

A higher land is Ireland![7]

This was not exactly Keats or Yeats, but I remembered reading a similar quatrain a few days earlier in the British Museum notesheets. I rushed to find Herring's edition. The poem, only slightly different, appeared on a "Cyclops" notesheet, and Joyce had crossed it out in red.[8] *Ulysses* does not include the poem, and I wondered if Joyce had used other crossed-out notes in the drafts in passages that he discarded before finishing the episode. I found some others in the draft but not enough to establish a pattern.

After a few days with this draft, I turned to the other "Cyclops" manuscript, a twenty-four-page copybook containing the four scenes from V.A.6 as well as four others. Spielberg described this copybook as a later document than the loose sheets of V.A.6 and gave it a higher number, V.A.8. The copybook is much more exciting to look at than V.A.6 but also harder to read: the handwriting is messier, and the additions sprawl all over many pages. The first four scenes here are not in V.A.6. Besides the unnamed characters (more than in the other draft) and the barely developed narrator, these scenes surprised me in two ways. First, the copybook starts with an opening for the episode but not with the distinctive first-person narrative voice familiar from the published "Cyclops." Instead, the draft's first words are an early version of a parody scene: "In ~~green Erin of the West~~ {Inisfail the fair} there lies a land, the land of holy Michan," a passage that appears seventy lines into the published episode.[9] The narrator is missing entirely from the first scene. Where was he? Also, on the back of the draft's first page appear several passages of Bloom's interior monologue as he walks along the streets between "Sirens" and "Cyclops."[10] The published text mentions his movements between the two episodes only indirectly, without indicating his thoughts.[11] Did Joyce once consider using interior monologue in "Cyclops"?

But the "Eureka!" moment for V.A.8 came with the final four scenes, the ones repeated from V.A.6. There again, on one of the copybook's more visually striking pages, were Stephen Dedalus's snide words about a Jew loving his country.[12] Surprisingly, I realized as I read, these scenes constituted not a later version of V.A.6 but an earlier one. Joyce had apparently rewritten the last four scenes of V.A.8 onto V.A.6's large pages, revising as he copied. Spielberg had misnumbered the two "Cyclops" documents and described them

(opposite page)
Milton Hebald (American, born 1917)
James Joyce, 1966
Miniature of original at Joyce's gravesite
in Fluntern Cemetery, Zurich
Sculpture, bronze
13 ½ x 7 x 5 ½

7. Buffalo MS V.A.6, 3v; *Notes*, 185; *Archive* 13:134f.

8. *Notesheets*, 92 ("Cyclops" notesheet 3:36-39); *Archive* 12:4.

9. Buffalo MS V.A.8, 1r; *Notes*, 152; *Archive* 13:85; *Ulysses* 12:68-70, 241.

10. Buffalo MS V.A.8, 1v-2r; *Notes*, 154; *Archive* 13:86-87.

11. See *Ulysses* 12:213-14, 244.

12. Buffalo MS V.A.8, 21r (Joyce misnumbered the page as 22); *Notes*, 170; *Archive* 13:125.

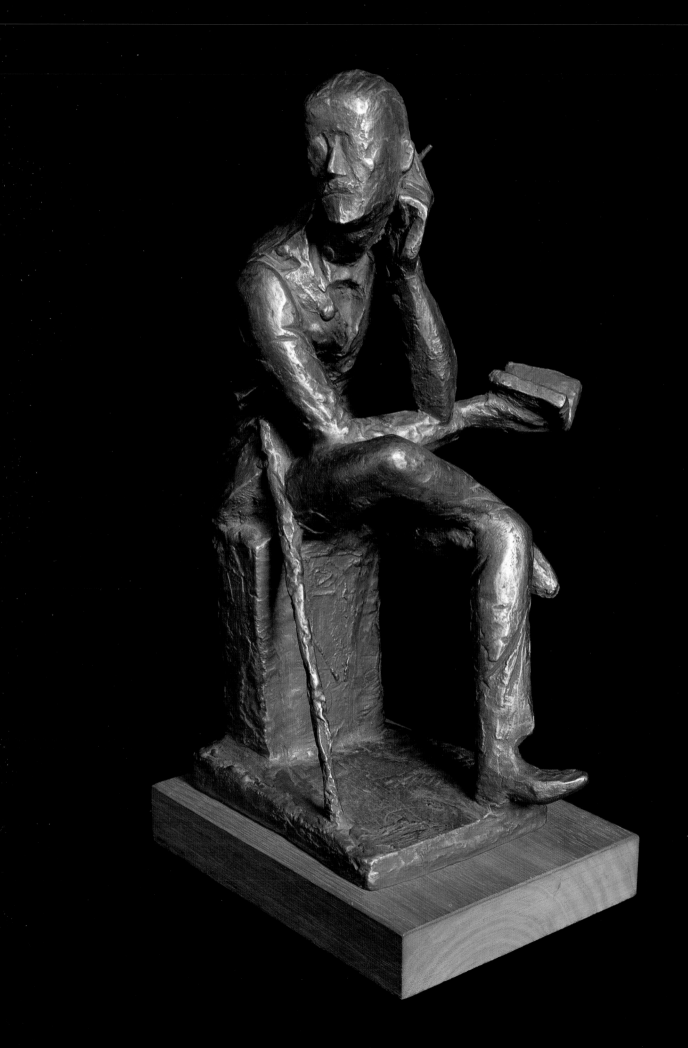

13. I learned a little later that I was not the only graduate student to notice Spielberg's misnumbering and incorrect description at this time. After I submitted my chapter on the "Cyclops" manuscripts to the *James Joyce Quarterly*, its editor, Thomas Staley, wrote me that, in addition to mine, he had almost simultaneously received another article about the documents. The *Quarterly* published both Myron Schwartzman's and my articles in the same issue. Luca Crispi's forthcoming online catalogue of the Buffalo Joyce Collection will offer a correct description of the "Cyclops" drafts and also include documents that Buffalo acquired after Spielberg prepared his catalogue in 1962.

(opposite page)
James Joyce, bearded, seated in profile, Zurich, 1919.

incorrectly, obscuring the relationship between them.[13] This copybook with its eight scenes was a very early draft, Joyce's first attempts to write the episode or close to them, and any possible pattern involving Joyce's color cross-outs would probably show up here. One did. Many notes that Joyce crossed out in red—including, among many others, "Inisfail the fair" (apparently a trigger for Joyce's replacement of "green Erin of the west" in the draft's opening words) and the remarks about a Jew loving his country and Bloom making up to his mother-in-law (both of which Joyce first used in this copybook)—appeared here, enough to establish that he crossed out notes simply to indicate that he had used them rather than to signify some kind of thematic connection among the notes or grouping of them.

As I worked on the "Cyclops" manuscripts, I clearly had a new thesis topic, and by the time I finished my chapter I was able to chart and describe the detailed sequence of Joyce's writing of "Cyclops" and his broader development of *Ulysses*. I went on to study Joyce's work on "Aeolus" and then his last years of work on *Ulysses* and postulated that his revision to *Ulysses* was less a sudden overhaul than an evolutionary development and that he moved gradually through three stages of work on *Ulysses*. This argument became the basis for my dissertation and then for my 1977 book *"Ulysses" in Progress*.

Why study a writer's manuscripts? Scholarly editors use them to investigate what went right and wrong as a work grew and proceeded towards publication so that they can establish a more accurate text than the author ever saw. But I was interested not in what went wrong but in how *Ulysses* developed. Manuscript study has been a part of Joyce scholarship since the start for several reasons: writers who knew Joyce, such as Frank Budgen, called attention to the documents; manuscripts became available quite early (*Stephen Hero* almost immediately after Joyce's death; the British Museum notesheets and *Finnegans Wake* manuscripts in the early 1950s; and the Buffalo, Cornell, and Yale collections in the late 1950s and early 1960s); and works as difficult as *Ulysses* and *Finnegans Wake* inspired scholars to try any approach that might possibly help. For many years, manuscript study was confined to a relatively small corner of Joyce scholarship. But new documents have come to light recently: drafts of "Circe" and "Eumaeus" in 2000 and 2001; a large group of early notes, notes for *Ulysses*, and drafts of individual *Ulysses* episodes in 2002; and, most recently, in 2006, some very early draft pages for *Finnegans Wake*. Except for the "Eumaeus" draft, which is in unknown private hands, the National Library of Ireland acquired all these documents, and they have attracted a great deal of attention and inspired new work which offers exciting discoveries and insights by asking traditional questions—how do the documents relate to each other, and what do they show about the ways Joyce wrote and revised *Ulysses*? what

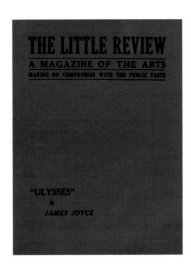

Fig. 20 Margaret Anderson and Jane Heap edited the *Little Review*, which published serialized installments of *Ulysses*.

14. For early investigations of some of the newly available materials, see Ronan Crowley on "Circe," Daniel Ferrer on "Proteus" and "Sirens," and Sam Slote on the "Circe," "Eumaeus," and *Wake* manuscripts, as well as my preliminary account of the NLI materials and Luca Crispi's forthcoming detailed online catalogue of that collection. English versions of some French genetic-criticism essays, both theoretical arguments and studies of specific authors, are in Jed Deppman, Daniel Ferrer, and Michael Groden, eds., *Genetic Criticism: Texts and Avant-textes*. A recent major project involving the *Finnegans Wake* Buffalo materials is *The "Finnegans Wake" Notebooks at Buffalo* edition.

15. For an elaboration of this claim, see my "Joyce at Work on 'Cyclops': Toward a Biography of *Ulysses*."

16. "one manifestation . . .": Louis Hay, "Does 'Text' Exist?" *Studies in Bibliography* 41 (1988): 64-76, originally in French in 1985. "series of potentialities": Michel Contat, Denis Hollier, and Jacques Neefs, "Editors' Preface," *Drafts*, special issue of *Yale French Studies* 89 (1986): 1-5. Both are quoted in Deppman, Ferrer, and Groden, eds., *Genetic Criticism*, 5-6.

are the sources for Joyce's notes, and how did he use these sources?—and also by following the lead of French theorists and practitioners of *critique génétique*, or genetic criticism (manuscript study's name today), who have applied various forms of literary study—narratology, linguistic analysis, psychoanalytic approaches, sociocriticism, deconstruction, gender theory—to manuscripts, the so-called *avant-texte* of a work, as well as to the published work.[14]

Knowing about how a work developed is certainly not necessary to enjoy and understand it—most readers lack this knowledge. But studying the manuscripts places the published text at the culmination of a long, complicated, and fascinating process, an artistic and also a very human one. *Ulysses* has changed greatly in the eighty-seven years since its publication, as the history of its criticism since 1922 instantly reveals. It also changed a lot as it developed from 1914 to 1922. Reading and studying the *avant-texte*, even the small "Cyclops" part, shows Joyce exploring possibilities; making mistakes and correcting them, often improving the text in the process; modifying his plans—all while living his life, moving from city to city, experiencing the World War and Irish War of Independence (even if at a distance), suffering through eye attacks, enduring lawsuits regarding theater costumes and various financial worries.[15] As with any work, the act of publication may have temporarily stopped the changing (although it hardly fixed the text, as any editor knows and the debates over the editions of *Ulysses* make clear), but ultimately it left the published version as "one manifestation of a process which is always virtually present in the background," a background which is also "a series of potentialities."[16] Genetic criticism brings to light and explores that background process, the obscured potentialities, in relation to the published text.

Authors are sometimes described as giving birth to their works, a problematic metaphor that might usefully be replaced by nurturer. (In France, where *Ulysses* was printed and published, the author signs off on the final set of proofs by writing "*bon à tirer*": the proofs are "good to pull," the text, fully grown, is ready to be published and released into the world.) Joyce was not the only nurturer of *Ulysses*: others include Ezra Pound, Margaret Anderson and Jane Heap (fig. 20), Sylvia Beach, Harriet Shaw Weaver, Maurice Darantiere, and later Judge John J. Woolsey and the book's American and English publishers. But the manuscripts reveal Joyce to be a wonderful primary nurturer of his texts as he takes notes, writes, revises, and corrects and augments proofs. The evidence for all this activity is in archives such as the Poetry Collection's, which serve as ongoing preservers and nurturers of Joyce's creative acts and each work's early life. Like *Ulysses* itself, the documents at Buffalo and in other collections await new readers who will struggle through them, marvel at their verbal and visual wonders, and make new discoveries about *Ulysses* and how its author wrote it.

Phonograph record of *Ulysses* (Paris: Shakespeare and Company, 1924). Signed by Joyce.

WORKS CITED

Crispi, Luca. Online catalogue of the James Joyce Collection at the National Library of Ireland. Forthcoming on the National Library of Ireland's Web site: http://www.nli.ie/.

———. Online catalogue of the James Joyce Collection. The Poetry Collection. The State University of New York at Buffalo. http://library.buffalo.edu/jamesjoyce/catalog/.

Crowley, Ronan. "Fusing the Elements of 'Circe.'" *James Joyce Quarterly*, forthcoming.

———. "'His Dark Materials': Joyce's 'Scribblings' and the Notes for 'Circe' in the National Library of Ireland." *Genetic Joyce Studies* 6 (2006). Online: http://www.antwerpjamesjoycecenter.com/GJS/GJS6/GJS6Crowley.htm.

Deppman, Jed, Daniel Ferrer, and Michael Groden, eds. *Genetic Criticism: Texts and Avant-textes*. Philadelphia: University of Pennsylvania Press, 2004.

Ferrer, Daniel. "What Song the Sirens Sang . . . Is No Longer Beyond All Conjecture: A Preliminary Description of the New 'Proteus' and 'Sirens' Manuscripts." *James Joyce Quarterly* 39, no. 1 (Fall 2001): 53-67.

Groden, Michael. "'Cyclops' in Progress, 1919." *James Joyce Quarterly* 12, no. 1-2 (Fall 1974-Winter 1975): 123-68.

———. "Joyce at Work on 'Cyclops': Toward a Biography of *Ulysses*." *James Joyce Quarterly* 44, no. 2 (Winter 2007): 217-45.

———. "The National Library of Ireland's New Joyce Manuscripts." In *Joyce in Trieste: An Album of Risky Readings*, edited by Sebastian D. G. Knowles, Geert Lernout, and John McCourt, 13-35. Gainesville: University Press of Florida, 2007.

———. *"Ulysses" in Progress*. Princeton, NJ: Princeton University Press, 1977.

Joyce, James. *The "Finnegans Wake" Notebooks at Buffalo*. Edited by Vincent Deane, Daniel Ferrer, and Geert Lernout. 12 vols. to date. Turnhout, Belgium: Brepols Publishers, 2001–.

———. *The James Joyce Archive*. Michael Groden, General Editor; Hans Walter Gabler, David Hayman, A. Walton Litz, and Danis Rose, Associate Editors. 63 vols. New York: Garland Publishing, 1977-79.

———. *Joyce's Notes and Early Drafts for "Ulysses": Selections from the Buffalo Collection*. Edited by Phillip F. Herring. Charlottesville: University Press of Virginia, 1977.

———. *Joyce's "Ulysses" Notesheets in the British Museum*. Edited by Phillip F. Herring. Charlottesville: University Press of Virginia, 1972.

———. *Ulysses: The Gabler Edition*. Edited by Hans Walter Gabler. New York: Vintage, 1986, 1993.

———. V: *Ulysses* Manuscripts. PCMS-020. James Joyce Collection. 1900-1959. The Poetry Collection, The State University of New York at Buffalo.

Litz, A. Walton. *The Art of James Joyce: Method and Design in "Ulysses" and "Finnegans Wake."* New York: Oxford University Press, 1961.

Schwartzman, Myron. "The V.A.8 Copybook: An Early Draft of the 'Cyclops' Chapter of *Ulysses* with Notes on Its Development." *James Joyce Quarterly* 12, no. 1-2 (Fall 1974-Winter 75): 64-122.

Slote, Sam. "Preliminary Comments on Two Newly-Discovered *Ulysses* Manuscripts." *James Joyce Quarterly* 39, no. 1 (Fall 2001): 17-28.

———. "Prolegomenon to the Development of Wakean Styles: New Acquisitions at the National Library of Ireland." *James Joyce Quarterly* 42-43, no. 1-4 (Fall 2004-Summer 2006): 21-30.

Spielberg, Peter, comp. *James Joyce's Manuscripts and Letters at the University of Buffalo: A Catalogue*. Buffalo: University of Buffalo, 1962.

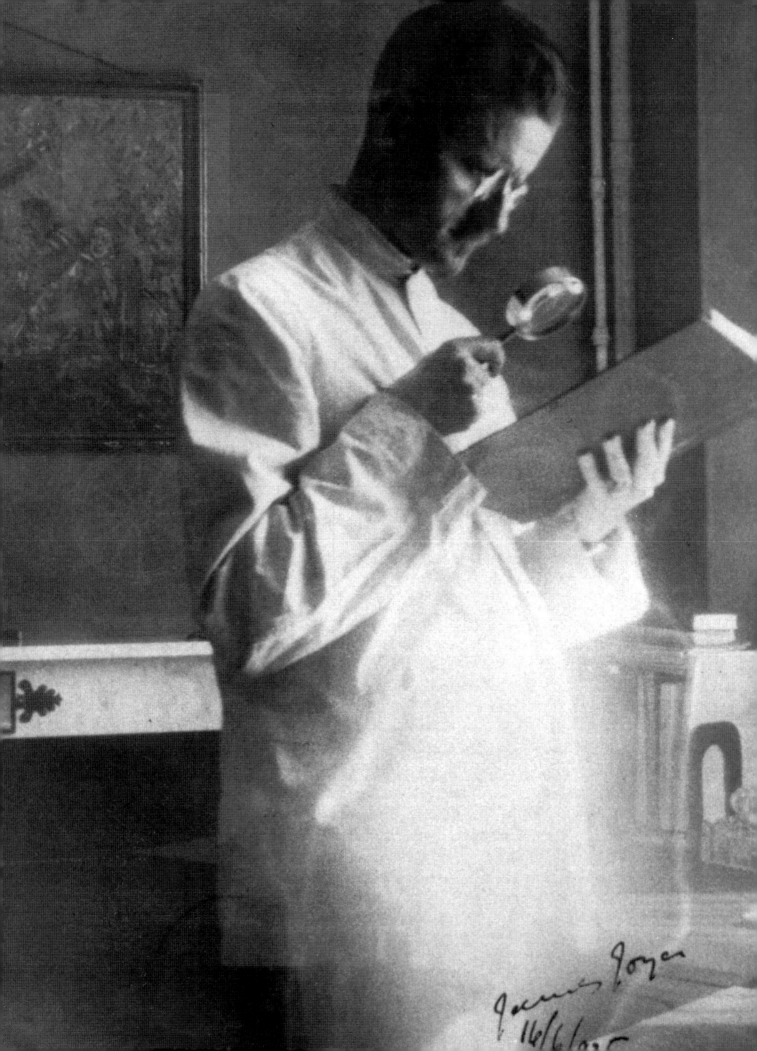

BUFFALO WAKES

Sam Slote

Writing is a messy business. A writer usually produces more than just the text that winds up published in the finished book: more work goes into a book than simply writing words on a page, page after page. For a book as complex as *Finnegans Wake* (fig. 21), this writerly effort is as clear as the readerly effort taken to try to understand just what Joyce was doing. Among other things, *Finnegans Wake* is an account of its gestation, and not just the final outcome or product of that gestation. Since it took Joyce seventeen years to write the *Wake*, he availed himself of the opportunity to incorporate all sorts of references to its composition within the text itself. For example, he responded to the various criticisms his work met with as it was being serialized in a variety of publications as well as incorporated its provisional pre-publication title *Work in Progress* into the text as "warping process," which could be construed as being a not-inaccurate description of Joyce's compositional style.[1] On his manuscripts Joyce frequently tagged insertions with the letter "F"; this compositional habit is itself described in the fifth chapter of the *Wake* and so one could say that Joyce was himself the first genetic critic of his works.

Fortunately, Joyce was not the last genetic critic of his works. More than twenty-five thousand manuscript pages for *Finnegans Wake* have survived. Since the published book itself has 628 pages, this means that there are, on average, forty pages of preparatory material for each page of final text. This figure, of course, only reflects documents that are extant, but fortunately the manuscript record for *Finnegans Wake* is quite comprehensive, at least when compared with the situation with *Ulysses* where many documents are still missing or unaccounted for.

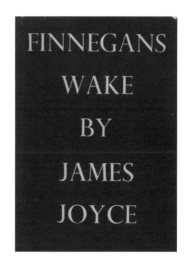

Fig. 21 *Finnegans Wake* (London: Faber and Faber, 1939).

(opposite page)
One of a series of photographs taken by Sylvia Beach on Bloomsday, 1925.

1. Joyce, *Finnegans Wake*, 497:3.

James Joyce's French identification card. It carried the visa permitting him to leave France, dated October 24, 1940.

Of the twenty-five thousand pages of preparatory material for the *Wake*, about fourteen thousand are at the Poetry Collection at Buffalo in the form of notebooks that Joyce compiled while writing his final book. Their survival is a testament to the dedication of Joyce's friend and personal secretary Paul Léon. At great personal risk and with much effort, Léon managed to keep Joyce's belongings—including his notebooks, personal library, and family portraits—secure from inquisitive Nazi officials and rapacious landlords after Joyce fled Paris in 1940 for Saint-Gérand-le-Puy and, eventually and finally, Zurich. Léon arranged to have Joyce's possessions stored safely at a lawyer's house before he was arrested and interned while visiting Paris to attend his son's graduation. He was killed in 1942.

Even before Léon's final act of service, Joyce signed his copy of *Finnegans Wake* with the following inscription out of gratitude for all his selfless work: "To that Eurasian Knight, Paul Léon, / with the Thousand and one thanks / of that most distressful writer, / James Joyce. / Paris, May 4th, 1939." All those who have benefitted from the material that Léon preserved should multiply those thanks by further thousands. Were it not for Léon and his dedication to Joyce there would be no collection of Joyce material at Buffalo and our understanding of the *Wake* would be much the poorer.

Fig. 22 *Finnegans Wake* notebook VI.B.10.

One might think that notebooks are a comparatively unimportant part of a writer's work, but Joyce explicitly linked his task of composing the *Wake* to the compilation of his notes. In 1929, when asked by Frank Crowninshield, the editor of *Vanity Fair*, how long he had been working on his new book Joyce tersely replied "7 years. Since October 1922. Begun at Nice."[2] Now, Joyce did not start writing material that wound up being incorporated into the *Wake* until March 1923, but in the autumn of 1922, while staying in Nice, he did begin taking notes. And so, for Joyce, the writing of the *Wake* began with his notes and not with the drafts. On 3 November 1922, Joyce sent his patron Harriet Shaw Weaver a list of corrections for *Ulysses* up to page 258, although he claimed that the list extended to page 290. The remaining corrections can be found in a small stenographer's notebook, now designated Buffalo notebook VI.B.10 (fig. 22). The first extant page of this notebook (eighty pages have fallen out and are missing) lists six corrections to the "Cyclops" episode. With the seventh entry, Joyce abruptly changes track and writes the curious line "Polyphemous is Ul[ysses]'s shadow."[3] Obviously this line was prompted by the episode of *Ulysses* he was correcting, but it is hardly an emendation. It is as if he is taking a step back to think about an aspect of the text he had just written and its relationship to its Homeric background. The remainder of the notes on this page are taken from the 20 October 1922 edition of the *Irish Times* and combine words from various sections of that paper. Three of these note-units from the *Irish Times* were eventually used in *Finnegans Wake*. On this one notebook page, we have Joyce leaving *Ulysses* behind in order to begin work on his newest book. And so the lexical work collected in the notebooks

2. Joyce, *Letters of James Joyce*, vol. 3, 193 and 193 n. 3.

3. Joyce, *The "Finnegans Wake" Notebooks*, Notebook *VI.B.10*, 18.

James Joyce with Ezra Pound, John Quinn, and Ford Madox Ford at Pound's Paris flat, circa 1923. This photograph commemorates the launch of the *Transatlantic Review*.

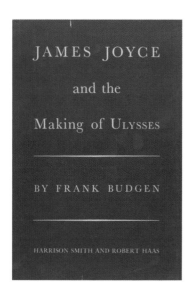

Fig. 23 Frank Budgen, *James Joyce and the Making of "Ulysses"* (New York: Harrison Smith and Robert Haas, 1934). This copy is inscribed by Budgen to Giorgio and Helen Joyce.

that leads into *Finnegans Wake* began by abandoning the task of emending or perfecting *Ulysses*. It is as if Joyce is saying: *Ulysses* cannot be corrected, hence *Finnegans Wake*.

Throughout his career, Joyce was an inveterate note-taker. Examples of his earlier note-taking survive, but it is only with *Finnegans Wake* that we have a near-complete record of his notes. The style of his notes is amazingly eclectic; he would attempt to gather any information that might somehow be relevant for his latest project. *Finnegans Wake*, like any literary work, is built from language, and Joyce used his notebooks to cull a wide variety of words and phrases he could use for his books. If *Finnegans Wake*, in all its bizarre encyclopedic mania, is a book of all earthly experience, then the notebooks served as Joyce's repository for the lexical local color of (seemingly) all earthly experiences. Joyce built a world, many worlds, from the words he gathered. Frank Budgen (fig. 23) described Joyce's note-taking habits for *Ulysses*:

> He was always looking and listening for the necessary fact or word; and he was a great believer in his luck. What he needed would come to him. That which he collected would prove useful in its time and place.... I have seen him collect in the space of a few hours the oddest assortment of material: a parody on the *House that Jack Built*, the name and action of a poison, the method of caning boys on training ships, the wobbly cessation of a tired unfinished sentence, the nervous tick of a convive turning his glass in inward-turning circles, a Swiss music-hall joke turning on a pun in Swiss dialect, a description of the Fitzsimmons shift.... At intervals, alone or in conversation, seated or walking, one of these tablets was produced, and a word or two scribbled on it at lightning speed as ear or memory served his turn. No one knew how all this material was given place in the completed pattern of his work.... The method of making a multitude of criss-cross notes in pencil was a strange one for a man whose sight was never good.[4]

A great deal of the *Wake's* verbiage likewise derives from notes taken from a variety of sources (newspapers, books, overheard conversation, etc.). In some cases, especially with the later notebooks, Joyce took the notes for specific purposes and in others he merely jotted down random words which were then subsequently used because they struck his fancy a second time, when he was going over his notebooks and preparing drafts. It appears that Joyce was amassing a heterogeneous stockpile of phrases in order to litter his work with all sorts of echoes of the world around him (of course, these echoes are almost impossible to identify without recourse to the notebooks). In this

4. Budgen, *James Joyce and the Making of "Ulysses,"* 175-77.

regard, Joyce really was "a scissors and paste man" as he admitted in 1931 to George Antheil.[5]

5. Joyce, *Letters of James Joyce*, vol. 1, 297.

Taken as a whole, Joyce's *Finnegans Wake* notebooks are visually quite beautiful (figs. 24, 25, 26). Like Budgen, one often wonders how they could have been used by someone with as notoriously bad an eyesight as Joyce. The colored-pencil cross-outs he would inflict on notebook entries once they had been used in order to preclude them from being harvested again lend the pages a striking appearance, even if this system was purely a pragmatic move conceived with no inclination towards aesthetic disposition. The colors Joyce chose for his cross-outs are apparently random and are not coded in any deliberate way. However, from the retrospective perspective of a notebook scholar they are useful since within any single notebook notes crossed out in one color would likely have been harvested at the same drafting session.

Beyond their visual appearance, the notebooks are quite beautiful to scholars because they literally provide a diary of the evolution of Joyce's conceptualizations for *Finnegans Wake* over the course of its lengthy composition. VI.B.10, the first *Wake* notebook, which began with his emendations for *Ulysses*, contains a wide variety of heterogeneous notes from various sources, mostly newspapers. There are a few consistent thematic clusters, such as notes on the Tristan and Isolde legend and notes on the Bywaters-Thompson murder trial,

Fig. 24 *Finnegans Wake* notebook VI.C.16.

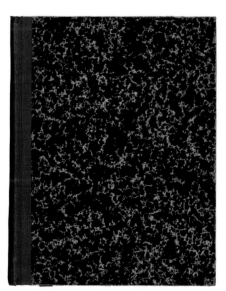

Fig. 25 *Finnegans Wake* notebook VI.C.9.

Fig. 26 *Finnegans Wake* notebook VI.B.34.

James Joyce seated on bench at
Fécamp, July 1925.

an infamous trial that took place in late 1922 in Britain, which inspired much
sensationalistic coverage in the press. However, the notes are mostly random:
Joyce was collecting material but apparently was unsure what purpose they
might eventually serve. The notes in the next notebook, designated VI.B.3, are
distinct in that they are somewhat more coherent thematically. As he becomes
more certain of what he's doing, the notes he takes become more and more
focused. Once Joyce began incorporating numerous foreign languages into the
Wake through trans-linguistic portmanteaux words, the notebooks proved an
invaluable repository of foreign words and phrases. Among other things, Joyce
was apparently particularly fond of collecting American slang expressions.
In notebook VI.B.37, as well as in others, he took notes from his lessons in
Russian, which he took from Léon's brother-in-law Alex Ponisovsky.

The notebooks were also used on occasion for making brief, rough drafts
of passages for the *Wake*, an example of which would be notebook VI.B.15,
from the second half of 1926, in which Joyce drafted the first hundred-

letter thunder-word that appears on the first page of *Finnegans Wake*. This one word collects together words that all mean "thunder" from a wide variety of languages, such as French, Greek, Irish Gaelic, Hindustani, Italian, Swedish, Portuguese, Old Rumanian, and so on, and, as such, is a perfect emblem of the role and purpose of the notebooks for Joyce's creative process.

From his earliest pre-*Wake* notebooks, Joyce used initials to designate various characters. By 1924, these had evolved into a set of curious signs, or, as they are now called, sigla (fig. 27)—some of these sigla appear on page 299 of *Finnegans Wake*. The sigla began as a kind of note-taking shorthand that Joyce used for the sake of convenience. In a later letter to Weaver, Joyce remarks that his friend, the French literary critic and author Valery Larbaud, laughed at these sigla when he first saw them, but Joyce explained, as a defense of his eccentric system, "it saves time."[6] Initially these sigla evolved as initials: the first sigla were stylized versions of the letters C and A, which were used for notes on Cain and Abel that Joyce took from a nineteenth-century Catholic commentary on the book of Genesis. These eventually became the sigla for Shem and Shaun, the *Wake's* squabbling fraternal couple. As Joyce continued to use the sigla, they evolved into graphic or iconic abstractions rather than being simply initials or abbreviations. For example, Joyce originally used the letters T and I to designate Tristan and Isolde. Eventually, the siglum for Isolde became an inverted T, thereby illustrating her relationship to Tristan as his partner and/or inverted reflection. As the character of Isolde evolved into a schizophrenic girl, Joyce began using a pair of sideways Ts as her sigla to designate her split personality.

The later notebooks, from the mid-1930s onwards, show Joyce's increasing mastery over his still-in-progress work. These last few notebooks contain notes organized under specific subject headings (or indices) such as *Huckleberry Finn*, Romansch, Basque, Burmese, Provençal, Hebrew, Russian, Chinese, Spanish, Polish, and Kissuaheli, among many others. At this late stage in the composition of the *Wake*, Joyce was looking for very specific things to add to his text and these notebooks served as an organizational repository for such items.

As he had done in 1922 with VI.B.10, Joyce did not stop taking notes once *Finnegans Wake* was finally published in 1939. The habit of note-taking seems to have been too firmly entrenched in his mind. In the second half of 1939, he filled up a small black imitation snakeskin notebook, VI.B.48, with mostly arbitrary jottings. He also used a 1940 pocket diary to record lists of American and French expressions, mostly slang (this is now item VIII.C.2 in the Buffalo collection). In their random style these entries resemble VI.B.10 but none of them are crossed out since none of them were ever used. If Joyce was contemplating writing a new work that would be—as he told George Pelorson in April 1939—"very simple and very short,"[7] this notebook gives no

Fig. 27 James Joyce, *Anna Livia Plurabelle* (New York: Crosby Gaige, 1928). The cover of this book features a variation of the siglum for the character of the same name.

6. Ibid., 216.

7. Ellmann, *James Joyce*, 731.

One of a series of photographs taken by Sylvia Beach on Bloomsday, 1925.

indication as to what that work might have been. And so, in between VI.B.10 and 48, Joyce wrote *Finnegans Wake*.

Joyceans slowly started to avail themselves of the *Finnegans Wake* notebooks as they became available in the 1950s. David Hayman, in the course of writing his dissertation on Joyce and Mallarmé, found that the *Wake* notebooks, then recently arrived at Buffalo, contained a wealth of material relevant to his study. In a lengthy appendix to his dissertation, Hayman includes a list of Mallarméan elements from the notebooks to help establish the fact of Joyce's familiarity with Mallarmé. As he was essentially the first scholar to publish a study of this as-yet-uncharted territory, his findings were, as he now admits, "crude." Since his dissertation, he has published much on the notebooks and *Wake* drafts and the increasing sophistication of our understanding of the notebooks derives, at least in part, from his engagement with these documents.

The next major work on the notebooks was Peter Spielberg's 1962 catalogue of the University of Buffalo's Joyce Collection. This involved the first sustained attempt at dating the *Finnegans Wake* notebooks; for this Spielberg collated notebook entries with the fragments of *Work in Progress* published from 1924 to 1938 (fig. 28). While his chronology is now known to be inaccurate, it was the first attempt to correlate the notebooks with other drafts. Since Spielberg's catalogue has been in use for so long, his numbering system is still employed, which is why the first *Finnegans Wake* notebook is catalogued as the tenth (VI.B.10). Luca Crispi's mammoth and meticulous revision of Spielberg's catalogue will soon be ready and for all this painstaking work we should give Crispi thanks.

Spielberg's dissertation advisor at Buffalo, Thomas E. Connolly, published a transcription of notebook VI.A, which he christened *Scribbledehobble* (fig. 29), after the first word of its text. He claimed that this notebook was the "Ur-workbook" for the *Wake* because of its large size and heterogeneity, although it is now known that this notebook postdates three others. Connolly took some care to annotate his transcriptions with indications of where the notebook entries were incorporated into the final text. Unfortunately his transcriptions are marked by inaccuracies and his attempts at indicating the color of Joyce's cross-outs were complicated by his color-blindness. His edition has been much criticized, but while it is of limited use it should nevertheless be recognized as a pioneer of notebook study.

In the 1960s, microfilm copies of both the Buffalo notebooks and the British Library *Wake* manuscripts began to circulate among a small number of Joyceans. This helped spark a small-scale interest in genetic matters, as can be seen in the trail-blazing journal *A Wake Newslitter*, which was founded in 1962 by Clive Hart and Fritz Senn. One of the *Newslitter's* contributors, Roland McHugh, published a revised version of Spielberg's notebook chronology in

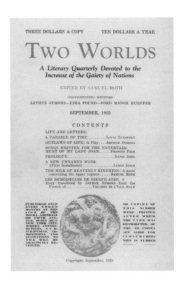

Fig. 28 An installment of *Work in Progress* appeared in *Two Worlds* 1, no. 1 (September 1925).

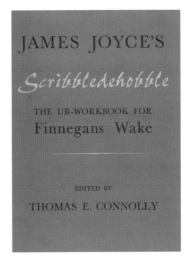

Fig. 29 Thomas E. Connolly, ed., *James Joyce's Scribbledehobble: The Ur-Workbook for "Finnegans Wake"* (Evanston, IL: Northwestern University Press, 1961).

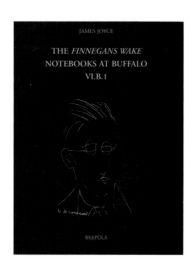

Fig. 30 *The "Finnegans Wake" Notebooks at Buffalo* edition of notebook VI.B.1 (Turnhout, Belgium: Brepols Publishers, 2003).

1972. His dating has since been revised further, first by David Hayman and Danis Rose for the *James Joyce Archive*, then by Rose for his book *The Textual Diaries of James Joyce*, and most recently by the editors of the ongoing *"Finnegans Wake" Notebooks at Buffalo* (fig. 30) series.

Because of all this work, and much other besides, the *Finnegans Wake* notebooks are now no longer a daunting morass of scribbles and colored cross-outs. We can recognize in them all the work and care and toil that Joyce employed while planning and writing *Finnegans Wake*. And in them we can also recognize all the work and care and toil that several generations of Joyceans have employed while reading, or trying to read, *Finnegans Wake*.

WORKS CITED

Budgen, Frank. *James Joyce and the Making of "Ulysses."* Oxford: Oxford University Press, 1989.

Ellmann, Richard. *James Joyce.* Rev. ed. Oxford: Oxford University Press, 1982.

Joyce, James. *Finnegans Wake.* London: Faber and Faber; New York: Viking, 1939.

———. *The "Finnegans Wake" Notebooks at Buffalo. Notebook VI.B.10.* Edited by Vincent Deane, Daniel Ferrer, and Geert Lernout. Turnhout, Belgium: Brepols Publishers, 2001.

———. *Letters of James Joyce.* Vol. 1. Edited by Stuart Gilbert. London: Faber and Faber, 1957.

———. *Letters of James Joyce.* Vol. 3. Edited by Richard Ellmann. London: Faber and Faber, 1966.

One of a series of photographs taken by Sylvia Beach on Bloomsday, 1925.

Joyce family crest
No date
Paint and ink on paper
8 x 6 ⅛

JOYCE FAMILY PHOTOGRAPHS

The Poetry Collection's Joyce photographs are a combination of those photographs that belonged to the Joyce family and came to Buffalo in the Wickser consignment and those that belonged to Sylvia Beach and came to Buffalo in the Stafford consignments. Many of Sylvia Beach's photographs were given to her as gifts by Joyce and many are, therefore, signed by Joyce. They were displayed in Shakespeare and Company and later in Sylvia Beach's Paris apartment. The photographers of those shown here are unknown.

James Joyce, age 3, 1885.

James Joyce in sailor suit, age 6, 1888.

James Joyce with his mother, father, and maternal grandfather at age 6, 1888.

James Joyce, graduation from Royal University (later University College Dublin), 1902.

Lucia and Giorgio Joyce with kitten standing at the window, Trieste, 1910.

James Joyce with hat, Zurich, 1912.

Formal portrait of Nora Joyce, standing, wearing white dress and gloves, Zurich, 1914.

Formal portrait of Nora Joyce, seated, wearing black hat, Zurich, 1914.

Nora Joyce with Giorgio and Lucia, Zurich, 1918.

Formal portrait of Joyce family, 1924.

Nora Joyce seated indoors, Ostend, 1924.

James and Lucia Joyce, Brittany, 1924.

James Joyce with Nora and Moune Gilbert, Zurich, 1929.

James Joyce, James Stephens, and John Sullivan walking on rue Raspail, Paris, 1929.

Giorgio Joyce, circa 1930.

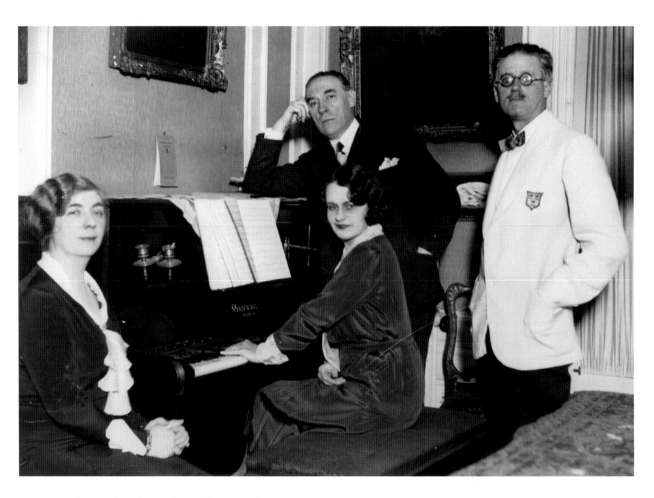

James Joyce with Nora, John Sullivan, and Mrs. Sullivan grouped at piano, 1930.

James and Nora Joyce in London on their way to be married, July 4, 1931.

James Joyce with Nora, Lucia, and unidentified little girl at table in garden, 1932.

Mrs. May Joyce Monaghan, Joyce's sister, at Lockwood Memorial Library, 1964.

EXHIBITION CHECKLIST

All dimensions are in inches, with height preceding width.

* indicates items reproduced in the catalogue.

Catalogue numbers for the James Joyce Collection are based on the scholarly work of Peter Spielberg and Luca Crispi. Much but not all of the manuscript material was first described in Spielberg's *James Joyce's Manuscripts and Letters at the University of Buffalo: A Catalogue* (Buffalo: University of Buffalo, 1962). More recently, Crispi has been revising, updating, and completing Spielberg's catalogue to reflect additions to the collection, contemporary Joyce scholarship, and his own research. Although still in process, *The UB James Joyce Catalogue* is available online (http://library.buffalo.edu/jamesjoyce/catalog). Brackets indicate the original Spielberg numbering, while unbracketed numbers refer to Crispi's revised order; to avoid ambiguity, the page numbers following these catalogue numbers belong to each scholar's respective system of pagination. The unbracketed roman numerals (Crispi) correspond to the following sections of the James Joyce Collection:

I. Epiphanies

II. *A Portrait of the Artist as a Young Man*

III. *Exiles*

IV. Verses

V. *Ulysses*

VI. *Finnegans Wake*

VII. Criticism

VIII. Miscellaneous Notebooks

IX. Miscellaneous Manuscripts

X. Correspondence from James Joyce

XI. Correspondence to James Joyce

XII. Correspondence from Sylvia Beach

XIII. Correspondence to Sylvia Beach and Shakespeare and Company

XIV. Correspondence from Imprimerie Darantiere to Sylvia Beach/James Joyce

XV. Correspondence of Lucia Joyce

XVI. Other Correspondents

XVII. Photographs and Portraits

XVIII. Miscellaneous Material Related to Joyce's Works

XIX. Miscellaneous James Joyce Material

XX. Miscellaneous Sylvia Beach and Shakespeare and Company Material

XXI. Miscellaneous Lucia Joyce Material

XXII. Other Miscellaneous Material

Origins

✻ *Exposition en Hommage à James Joyce*, 1949
Librairie La Hune poster advertising "James Joyce:
Sa Vie, Son Œuvre, Son Rayonnement"
Printed poster, Paris
23 ⅜ x 15 ½

✻ Map of Dublin on June 16, 1904
Librairie La Hune, 1949
Prepared map, Paris
56 x 110 ¼

✻ Series of images from *Exposition en Hommage à James Joyce*, 1949
Photographs, black and white (unknown)
Various sizes

First Editions and Photographs

Chamber Music
London: Elkin Matthews, 1907

✻ Constantine P. Curran (Irish)
James Joyce, Dublin, 1904
Photograph, black and white
6 x 4 ½

Dubliners
London: Grant Richards, 1914

James Joyce seated, Zurich, 1914
Photograph, black and white (unknown)
8 ⅛ x 6 ¼

Exiles
London: Grant Richards, 1918

✻ James Joyce, bearded, seated in profile, Zurich, 1919
Photograph, black and white (unknown)
9 ⅜ x 6 ¾

A Portrait of the Artist as a Young Man
New York: B. W. Huebsch, 1916

✻ James Joyce, seated, playing guitar, Zurich, 1915
Photograph, black and white (unknown)
6 ⅞ x 9 ¾

Ulysses
Paris: Shakespeare and Company, 1922
Copy no. 800, inscribed by Sylvia Beach to
Constance and Walter Stafford

Ulysses
Paris: Shakespeare and Company, 1922
Copy no. 1000, inscribed by James Joyce to his wife, Nora

James Joyce with Sylvia Beach, Cyprian Beach,
and John Rodker at Shakespeare and Company, 1921
Photograph, black and white (unknown)
6 ⅞ x 10

✻ *Finnegans Wake*
London: Faber and Faber, 1939

Carola Giedion-Welcker (Swiss, 1893–1979)
James Joyce, Place Spitz, Zurich, 1938
Photograph, black and white
8 ¼ x 5 ¾

Joyce Family Portraits

✻ Patrick Tuohy (Irish, 1894–1930)
James Joyce, circa 1924
Oil on canvas
24 x 19 ¾

✻ John Comerford (Irish, flourished 1800s), *attrib. by James Joyce*
James Joyce (1800–1855?), circa 1845
Joyce's paternal great-grandfather
Oil on canvas
30 x 25

✻ John Comerford (Irish, flourished 1800s), *attrib. by James Joyce*
Anne McCann Joyce, circa 1845
Joyce's paternal great-grandmother
Oil on canvas
30 ¼ x 25

✼ Frank Budgen (British, 1882–1971)
Nora Barnacle Joyce, circa 1919
Joyce's wife
Oil on paperboard
22 ⅛ x 17 ⅝

✼ John Comerford (Irish, flourished 1800s), *attrib. by James Joyce*
James Augustine Joyce (1827–1866), circa 1855
Joyce's paternal grandfather
Oil on canvas
30 x 25

✼ John Comerford (Irish, flourished 1800s), *attrib. by James Joyce*
Ellen O'Connell Joyce (1816–1881), circa 1845
Joyce's paternal grandmother
Oil on canvas
30 x 25

✼ John Comerford (Irish, flourished 1800s), *attrib. by James Joyce*
James Augustine Joyce (1827–1866), circa 1845
Joyce's paternal grandfather, as a young man
Oil on canvas
25 ½ x 19 ½

✼ Patrick Tuohy (Irish, 1894–1930)
John Stanislaus Joyce (1849–1931), circa 1924
Joyce's father
Oil on canvas
39 ½ x 32

✼ Tullio Silvestri (Italian, 1880–1963)
James Joyce, 1914
Watercolor on paper
19 ¼ x 15 ⅛

✼ Tullio Silvestri (Italian, 1880–1963)
Nora Barnacle Joyce, 1914
Joyce's wife
Oil on burlap
35 ½ x 29 ½

✼ Patrick Tuohy (Irish, 1894–1930)
Mary Joyce (1859–1903), 1926
Joyce's mother
Pencil on paper
16 ½ x 12 ⅝

✼ Patrick Tuohy (Irish, 1894–1930)
Lucia Joyce (1907–1982), 1927
Joyce's daughter
Pencil on paper
15 x 12

✼ Joyce family crest
No date
Paint and ink on paper
8 x 6 ⅛

✼ Joyce family coat of arms
No date
Paint and ink on paper
14 ¾ x 11

✼ Constantin Brancusi (Romanian, 1876–1957)
James Joyce, 1929
Pencil on paper
8 ¼ x 6 ¼

Wyndham Lewis (British, 1882–1957)
Charles D. Abbott, 1939
First library director, University of Buffalo
Pencil on paper
17 ¾ x 11 ¾

Wyndham Lewis (British, 1882–1957)
Theresa Abbott, 1939
Pencil on paper
17 ¾ x 11 ¾

Joyce Family Photographs

✼ James Joyce, age 3, 1885
Photograph, black and white (unknown)
Signed by Joyce
3 ¾ x 2 ½

✼ James Joyce with his mother, father,
and maternal grandfather, 1888
Photograph, black and white (unknown)
Signed by Joyce
8 ⅛ x 5 ½

* James Joyce in sailor suit, age 6, 1888
Photograph, black and white (unknown)
Signed by Joyce
5 ¾ x 4 ¼

James Joyce and school friends George Clancy
and J. F. Byrne, 1900–1901
Photograph, black and white (unknown)
Signed by Joyce
5 ¾ x 4

* James Joyce's graduation from
Royal University (later University College Dublin), 1902
Photograph, black and white (unknown)
Signed by Joyce
5 ¾ x 4

James Joyce in hat and great coat, Zurich, 1914
Photograph, black and white (unknown)
Signed by Joyce
4 ¼ x 2 ¾

* James Joyce, bearded, three-quarter view, Zurich, 1919
Photograph, black and white (unknown)
9 ⅜ x 6 ¾

James Joyce with moustache, 1915
Photograph, black and white (unknown)
Signed by Joyce
3 ⅝ x 2 ½

James Joyce with moustache, close up, 1915
Photograph, black and white (unknown)
3 ¼ x 2 ¼

* Giorgio and Lucia Joyce, Trieste, 1910
Photograph, black and white (unknown)
3 x 4 ¼

Lucia Joyce in group school photograph, Trieste, 1910
Photograph, black and white (unknown)
5 ¼ x 9 ⅛

* Nora with Giorgio and Lucia Joyce, Zurich, 1918
Photograph, black and white (unknown)
4 x 2 ⅝

* Nora Joyce with hat, Zurich, 1914
Photograph, black and white (unknown)
5 ¾ x 4 ⅛

* Nora Joyce standing, Zurich, 1914
Photograph, black and white (unknown)
6 x 4

James Joyce and Sylvia Beach seated
at Shakespeare and Company, 1921
Photograph, black and white (unknown)
6 ½ x 8 ¾

* James Joyce and Sylvia Beach seated
at Shakespeare and Company, 1922
Photograph, black and white (unknown)
6 ¼ x 9 ½

Berenice Abbott (American, 1898–1991)
James Joyce, eyes closed, Paris, 1926
Photograph, black and white
9 ⅜ x 7

Nora Joyce seated on steps, Ostend, 1924
Photograph, black and white (unknown)
3 ½ x 2 ¼

* Nora Joyce seated indoors, Ostend, 1924
Photograph, black and white (unknown)
2 ⅜ x 3 ½

Lucia Joyce and friends in dance costumes, 1928
Photograph, black and white (unknown)
Inscribed to Sylvia Beach by Lucia Joyce
5 ⅜ x 3 ⅜

Lucia Joyce's sketchbook
XXI. Folder 11
Tinted charcoal on paper
12 ½ x 9 ½

Les Ballets Rythme et Couleur, circa 1926–1928
XXI. Folder 3
Dance program
9 ⅜ x 6 ⅛

Lucia Joyce in profile, dance pose, 1928
Photograph, black and white (unknown)
7 x 5 ⅜

Lucia Joyce standing, Ostend, 1924
Photograph, black and white (unknown)
3 ½ x 2 ½

Nora and Giorgio Joyce, Ostend, 1924
Photograph, black and white (unknown)
2 ½ x 3 ½

Lucia Joyce seated at table, Ostend, 1924
Photograph, black and white (unknown)
2 ½ x 3 ¾

✻ Joyce family, formal portrait, 1924
Photograph, black and white (unknown)
Signed by Joyce
9 ⅜ x 7

Giorgio Joyce, circa mid-1920s
Photograph, black and white (unknown)
3 ⅜ x 2 ⅜

✻ James and Lucia Joyce, Brittany, 1924
Photograph, black and white (unknown)
2 ¼ x 3 ⅛

James Joyce and John Drinkwater, Salzburg, 1928
Photograph, black and white (unknown)
7 ¼ x 4 ½

Berenice Abbott (American, 1898–1991)
James Joyce seated, hand to chin, 1929
Photograph, black and white
9 ¾ x 7 ¾

Berenice Abbott (American, 1898–1991)
James Joyce seated with cane, 1929
Photograph, black and white
9 ⅝ x 7 ¾

Berenice Abbott (American, 1898–1991)
James Joyce seated, hands clasped, 1929
Photograph, black and white
9 ¾ x 8

Man Ray (American, 1890–1976)
Giorgio Joyce and his wife,
Helen Fleischman Joyce, 1930
Photograph, black and white
5 ¾ x 3 ¾

James Joyce and John Sullivan, 1938
Photograph, black and white (unknown)
9 ⅜ x 7 ⅛

James Joyce, John Sullivan, and James Stephens, Paris, 1938
Photograph, black and white (unknown)
9 ½ x 7 ⅛

James Joyce, John Sullivan, and James Stephens, Paris, 1938
Photograph, black and white (unknown)
7 ¼ x 9 ¼

Gisèle Freund (German, 1908–2000)
James and Giorgio Joyce by piano, 1938
Photograph, black and white
4 ¼ x 5 ⅝

Gisèle Freund (German, 1908–2000)
James with Giorgio, Helen, and Stephen James Joyce, 1938
Photograph, black and white
5 ¾ x 4

✻ James Joyce's passport, 1924
XIX. Folder 10
6 x 4 ¼

James Joyce's passport, 1935
XIX. Folder 32
6 x 4 ¼

James Joyce's glasses and case
XIX. Folder 28

Joyce's Private Library

W. B. Yeats
The Collected Poems
London: Macmillan, 1934
Inscribed, signed, and dated by the author

Flann O'Brien [Brian O'Nolan]
At Swim-Two-Birds
London; New York: Longmans, Green and Co., 1939
Inscribed and signed by the author

James Stephens
Kings and the Moon
New York: The Macmillan Company, 1938
Inscribed and signed by the author

Ezra Pound
A Draft of XXX Cantos
Paris: Hours Press, 1930
Inscribed and signed by the author

T. S. Eliot
The Waste Land
New York: Boni and Liveright, 1922
Copy no. 405 of 1000
Inscribed and signed by the author

Ernest Hemingway
A Farewell to Arms
New York: Scribner, 1929
Inscribed and signed by the author

Padraic Colum
The Adventures of Odysseus and the Tale of Troy
New York: Macmillan Company, 1918
Inscribed and signed by the author

Ezra Pound
Indiscretions, or, Une revue de deux mondes
Paris: Three Mountains Press, 1923
Copy no. 58 of 300
Inscribed and signed by the author

Joyce's dress cane
XIX. Folder 4
Ebony and ivory cane with engraved J
36 ¼

Joyce's cane
XIX. Folder 4
Wooden cane with metal band engraved JJ
36 ¼

Joyce's cane
XIX. Folder 4
Wooden cane
36 ¼

Nancy Cox-McCormack Cushman (American, 1885–1967)
Ezra Pound, 1923
Sculpture, plaster
9 ¾ x 10 x 4 ¼

Horst Tappe (German, 1938–2005)
Ezra Pound visiting Joyce's grave, Zurich, 1967
Photograph, black and white
8 x 10

✻ Milton Hebald (American, born 1917)
James Joyce, 1966
Miniature of original at Joyce's gravesite
in Fluntern Cemetery, Zurich
Sculpture, bronze
13 ½ x 7 x 5 ½

Early Works

Two Essays (two copies displayed)
Dublin: printed by Gerrard Bros., 1901

✻ "A Portrait of the Artist" essay
[II.A]
Notebook
6 ⅞ x 9 ⅛

James Joyce to B. W. Huebsch, October 24, 1916
X.M.3 [X.E.3]
Holograph letter
10 ½ x 8 ⅛

Epiphany no. 1. "Pull out his eyes…"
[I.A]
Holograph, single sheet of ruled paper
9 ½ x 7 ⅜

Corrections for *A Portrait of the Artist as a Young Man*
in Harriet Shaw Weaver's hand
[II.C.1]
Single sheet of ruled paper
13 x 8 ⅛

Exiles notebook
[III.A]
11 ⅛ x 9

Gas from a Burner
Broadside poem
[Trieste: The Author], 1912
30 x 12

James Joyce to Grant Richards, January 16, 1905
X.Z.1
Typed letter, unsigned
10 x 8

The Holy Office
Broadside poem
[Pola, Italy: The Author, 1904]
11 ⅜ x 8 ¾

The Transition to *Ulysses*

Notebook
V.A.2.a [VIII.A.5]
A Zurich notebook
6 ⅞ x 4 ¼

Notebook
[VIII.A.1]
A Zurich notebook
8 ¾ x 7

Notebook
[VIII.A.3]
A Zurich notebook
6 ¾ x 4 ¼

Notebook
[VIII.A.4]
A Zurich notebook
6 ⅞ x 4 ⅜

Notebook, "Quaderno di James Joyce"
[VIII.B]
8 ½ x 7

Notebook, "Notes for the Episodes"
V.A.2.b [V.A.2]
9 ⅛ x 7 ½

Disbound notebook
V.A.4
Notes on Shakespeare
Three disbound sheets, including front cover
Each 8 ¾ x 13 ¾

Ulysses Drafts

Proteus notebook
V.A.3
Four sheets from a disbound notebook that contained
a draft of the Proteus chapter of *Ulysses*
Each 8 ¾ x 13 ¾

Cyclops chapter
V.A.6
Two foolscaps; early drafts of the Cyclops chapter of *Ulysses*
Each 14 ½ x 17 ¾

Cyclops notebook
V.A.8
Four sheets from a disbound notebook that contained
a draft of the Cyclops chapter of *Ulysses*
Each 8 ½ x 13 ¾

Oxen of the Sun notebook
V.A.11
Three sheets from a disbound notebook that contained
a draft of the Oxen of the Sun chapter of *Ulysses*
Each 9 ½ x 15 ¼

Eumaeus notebook
V.A.21
Three sheets from a disbound notebook that contained
a draft of the Eumaeus chapter of *Ulysses*
Each 7 ½ x 11 ½

Penelope chapter
V.A.22
Five sheets, fair copy, holograph; the final pages of *Ulysses*
Each 12 x 7 ¾

Cyclops chapter
V.B.10.a.i p22 [V.B.10.a]
Typescript, one page
10 ¾ x 8 ½

Penelope chapter
V.B.16.b.i p23 [V.B.16.c p23]
Typescript, one page
10 ½ x 8 ¼

Calypso chapter
V.B.3.a.ii p1 [V.B.3.b]
Typescript, one page
10 ¾ x 8 ⅜

Hades chapter
V.B.4 p11
Typescript, one page
11 x 8 ½

Proteus chapter
V.B.2 p1
Typescript, one page
11 x 8 ¾

Ithaca chapter
V.B.15c p56
Piece of cut-out music
4 ¾ x 6 ⅝

Ithaca chapter
V.B.15c p58
Small piece of music
2 ⅝ x 8 ¼

Ithaca chapter
V.B.15c p57
Typescript, one page
Page with music clipped away
10 ½ x 8 ¼

James Joyce to Claude Sykes, December 19, 1917
X.Z.D
Postcard
5 ½ x 3 ½

James Joyce to John Quinn, February 4, 1924
X.Y.1
Holograph draft and typed final version of letter
10 ⅝ x 8 ¼

Placard
V.C.1.B.4.ii.a [V.C.4]
One sheet: "The Banwasser at Work"
with the Darantiere stamp
18 ½ x 29

* *The Little Review*
Twenty-three magazine issues
Joyce's copies

Man Ray (American, 1890–1976)
Margaret Anderson and Jane Heap,
editors of the *Little Review*
Photograph, black and white
3 ½ x 5 ½

Wyndham Lewis (British, 1882–1957)
Harriet Shaw Weaver, 1925
Pencil on paper
24 x 20

The Evolution of Circe

Circe notebook
V.A.19
Eight sheets from a disbound notebook that contained
a draft of the Circe chapter of *Ulysses*
Each 8 ¼ x 13

Circe holograph pages
V.A.20
Three hand-written pages of the Circe chapter of *Ulysses*
Each 12 ¾ x 7 ¼

Stages of Circe
V.B.13.h.2 pp1, 5, 10; V.B.13.h.6 p1; V.B.13.h.3 p20; V.B.13.e.I pp35,
44; V.B.13.a p1; V.B.13.b p1; V.B.13.c p1; V.B.13.d.10 p2; V.B.13.d.I p54
Twelve typescript and holograph pages of the Circe chapter of *Ulysses*
Most 10 ½ x 8 ½

Circe page proofs
V.C.2.B.21.i [V.C.1.30.a]; V.C.2.B.21.ii [V.C.1.30.b]
Twelve units in total; pages 476/469, 460/453
Each 14 ½ x 9

James Joyce to Sylvia Beach, April 13, 1921
X.C.3 [X.B.I]
Holograph letter, written on the back of Joyce's calling card
2 ¾ x 4

✳ *Ulysses*
Paris: Shakespeare and Company, 1922

Ulysses
Paris: Shakespeare and Company, 1922
Second printing

Ulysses
Paris: Shakespeare and Company, 1922
Third printing

The Production of *Ulysses*

Maurice Darantiere to Sylvia Beach, April 18, 1921
XIV.3
Typed letter
10 ⅝ x 8 ½

Maurice Darantiere to Sylvia Beach, June 9, 1921
XIV.9
Typed letter
10 ½ x 8 ¼

Maurice Hirschwald to Sylvia Beach, October 11, 1921
XIV.38
Holograph letter, two leaves
Each 7 ¾ x 5 ¼

Maurice Hirschwald to Sylvia Beach, August 11, 1921
XIV.21
Holograph letter
8 ¼ x 10 ¼

Maurice Darantiere to Sylvia Beach, June 16, 1921
XIV.10
Typed letter
10 ½ x 8 ¼

Maurice Darantiere to Sylvia Beach, November 3, 1921
XIV.42
Typed letter
10 ½ x 8 ¼

Maurice Darantiere to Sylvia Beach, November 29, 1921
XIV.49
Typed letter
10 ½ x 8 ¼

Maurice Darantiere to Sylvia Beach, January 17, 1922
XIV.60
Typed letter
10 ½ x 8 ¼

Imprimerie Kapp to Sylvia Beach, April 22, 1921
XIII. Kapp to Beach
Typed letter
10 ¾ x 8 ½

James Joyce to Maurice Hirschwald, [late 1921]
X.L [X.J.I]
Holograph letter
8 ⅛ x 10 ½

James Joyce's draft of front matter for *Ulysses*
V.D.2.b; V.D.2.a [V.D.I.a; V.D.I.b]
Eleven leaves in total
Each approx. 10 ½ x 8 ½

First prototype book cover for *Ulysses*
XVIII.E1. Folder 14
12 x 18 ¾

Final proof cover for *Ulysses*
XVIII.E1. Folder 14.b
15 ⅛ x 22 ¼

Completed *Ulysses* subscription forms
XVIII.E1. Folder 13
Forms from W. B. Yeats, W. C. Williams, Samuel Roth,
T. E. Lawrence, H. S. Weaver, P. Guggenheim
Each 6 ½ x 8 ½

Adrienne Monnier's holograph draft of *Ulysses* prospectus
XVIII.E1. Folder 4
8 ¼ x 5 ¼

Three emended *Ulysses* prospecti
* 1st – rue Dupuytren
XVIII.E1. Folder 9
2nd – rue d'Odéon (is now ready)
XVIII.E1. Folder 10
3rd – rue d'Odéon (emended date)
XVIII.E1. Folder 11
Each 8 ½ x 6 ½

"*Ulysses* by James Joyce is now ready" card, 1922
XVIII.E1. Folder 16
5 x 6 ¾

"*Ulysses* by James Joyce is sold out" card, 1922
XVIII.E1. Folder 22
4 ¾ x 6 ¾

Shakespeare and Company lending library card
XX. Folder 3
3 ½ x 4 ⅛

Sylvia Beach's accounting diary, 1921–1922
XX. Folder 5
5 ¾ x 3 ¾

James Joyce's holograph list of potential subscribers
XVIII.E1. Folder 7
15 ¾ x 12 ¼

James Joyce's holograph list of potential subscribers
with addresses, circa 1921
XVIII.E1. Folder 8
12 ½ x 7 ¾

Two-page holograph list of potential subscribers
in James and Lucia Joyce's hand
XVIII.E1. Folder 8
Each 10 ½ x 8 ¼

James Joyce's extract of Ezra Pound's article for press notice
XVIII.E1. Folder 6
8 x 8 ¼

James Joyce's extracts from press notices
XVIII.E1. Folder 5
Holograph in Joyce's hand
7 ¾ x 6 ⅛

Extracts from press notices
XVIII.E1. Folder 24
Printed document
9 ½ x 6 ½

Maurice Darantiere to Sylvia Beach, January 28, 1922
XIV.64
Telegram
6 ⅞ x 9

Ulysses
Paris: Shakespeare and Company, 1922
First edition, copy no. 2 (Sylvia Beach's copy)
Signed and inscribed by James Joyce to Sylvia Beach

Maurice Darantiere to Sylvia Beach, February 2, 1922
XIV.68
Typed letter
10 ½ x 8 ¼

The pen James Joyce used to sign *Ulysses*
XVIII.E1. Folder 18
8 ½

Typed schema of *Ulysses*
V.A.1.b.i [V.A.1.b]
Signed and inscribed by James Joyce to Sylvia Beach
February 2, 1922
8 x 38

The Reception of *Ulysses*

Stuart Gilbert
James Joyce's "Ulysses"
London: Faber & Faber, 1930
Inscribed by Gilbert to James Joyce

✳ Frank Budgen
James Joyce and the Making of "Ulysses"
New York: Harrison Smith and Robert Haas, 1934
Inscribed by Budgen to Giorgio and Helen Joyce

Herbert Gorman
James Joyce
New York: B. W. Huebsch, 1924
James Joyce's copy

William C. Benson to Sylvia Beach, January 10, 1923
XIII. Benson to Beach
Holograph letter
10 ¼ x 6 ½

William Benson's business card
XIII. Benson to Beach
1 ¾ x 3 ¾

R. Burns to Sylvia Beach, April 9, 1923
XIII. Burns to Beach
Holograph letter
10 x 8

Ulysses
Industry, CA: Collectors Publications, 1960

✳ *Sporting Times:* "The Scandal of *Ulysses*"
XVIII.E1. Folder 19
Poster
30 x 20

Announcement for Valery Larbaud's talk about *Ulysses*
XVIII.E1. Folder 12
3 ⅛ x 5 ¼

The Criterion I, no. I (October 1922)

The Dial 72, no. 6 (June 1922)

René Maizeroy
Fleshly Attraction
Privately printed, 1921

"*Ulysses* in Omaha; Is Sex Stuff Waning?"
Unsigned news clipping from the Omaha, Nebraska
World Herald, 1927
15 ½ x 2 ¾

Later Printings of *Ulysses*

Ulysses errata
[V.F.20]
Five-page typescript
Each 10 x 8

Ulysses errata
[V.F.4]
A printed, emended set
9 x 7

Maurice Darantiere to Sylvia Beach, March 16, 1922
XIV.100
Typed letter, two pages
10 ¼ x 8 ¼

Ulysses
London: Egoist Press, 1922

Ulysses
Paris: Shakespeare and Company, 1924
Sylvia Beach's copy, inscribed by James Joyce

Announcement in French for the 1924 *Ulysses*
XVIII.E2. Folder 6
10 ¼ x 6 ½

✳ Phonograph record of *Ulysses*
XVIII.E2. Folder 8
Paris: Shakespeare and Company, 1924
Signed by Joyce
12 x 12

James Joyce's design for phonograph record label
XVIII.E2. Folder 7
8 ⅛ x10 ½

Ulysses
[New York: Samuel Roth, 1929]
First American edition (unauthorized)

Sylvia Beach's publication contract with James Joyce
XVIII.E2. Folder 10
9 ¾ x 6 ⅞

Ulysses
Hamburg; Paris; Bologna: Odyssey Press, 1932

Ulysses
New York: Random House, 1934
Sylvia Beach's copy, inscribed by James Joyce

Ulysses
New York: Limited Editions Club, 1935

Ulysses
London: John Lane the Bodley Head, 1936
Vellum-bound presentation copy, signed by James Joyce

Ulysses
San Francisco: Arion Press, 1988
Illustrated by Robert Motherwell (American, 1915–1991)

"How to Enjoy James Joyce's Great Novel *Ulysses*"
New York: Random House, 1934
8 x 5 ½ folded

James Joyce to Bennett Cerf, April 2, 1932
X.F [X.C.1]
Typed letter, two pages
12 ⅛ x 8 ¼

Envelope from James Joyce to Bennett Cerf letter
X.F [X.C.1]
5 x 6 ¼

Advertisement for the 1936 Bodley Head *Ulysses*
XVIII.E2. Folder 50
11 ¼ x 9

Advertisement for eighth printing of *Ulysses*
XVIII.E2. Folder 19
9 ¾ x 12 ¾

Advertisement for eleventh printing of *Ulysses*
XVIII.E2. Folder 43
9 ¾ x 6 ¾

Henri Matisse (French, 1869–1954)
Six signed etchings for the 1935
Limited Editions Club edition of *Ulysses*
Each 17 x 13

Two Worlds Monthly
Eleven issues
Vol. 1, nos. 1-4; vol. 2, nos. 1-4; vol. 3, nos. 1-3

French Translations of *Ulysses*

Protée, 1927
An off-print of the Proteus chapter's first appearance in French
9 x 5 ½

Ulysse
Paris: La Maison des Amis des Livres, 1929
Sylvia Beach's copy, inscribed by James Joyce

Ulysse postcard
XVIII.E2. Folder 13
5 ½ x 3 ½

Menu for Déjeuner *Ulysse*
XVIII.E2. Folder 39
6 ¼ x 4 ⅝

✻ Announcement for the French translation of *Ulysses*
XVIII.E2. Folder 34
10 x 6 ¼

Catalogue in which the French translation
of *Ulysses* was advertised
XVIII.E2. Folder 37
8 ½ x 6 ½

Subscription form for the French translation of *Ulysses*
XVIII.E2. Folder 35
8 ¾ x 5 ½

Pomes Penyeach

Pomes Penyeach notebook
IV.A.1
8 ¾ x 7

✳ *Pomes Penyeach*
Paris: Shakespeare and Company, 1927
First edition

Pomes Penyeach
Princeton, NJ: Princeton University Press for Sylvia Beach, 1931

Pomes Penyeach
Paris: The Obelisk Press, 1932

Shakespeare and Company advertisement
for *Ulysses* and *Pomes Penyeach*
XVIII.F. Folder 6
5 x 5 ¼

Lucia Joyce's scrapbook
XXI. Folder 9
9 x 20 ¾

Specimens of Lucia Joyce's work
XXI. Folder 16
Three objects
Each approx. 3 x 3

Finnegans Wake

Finnegans Wake Scribbledehobble notebook
[VI.A]
10 x 7 ¼ x 2 ½

Finnegans Wake notebook 1
[VI.B.1]
8 ¼ x 5 ¼

Finnegans Wake notebook 2
[VI.B.2]
7 ½ x 5 ¼

Finnegans Wake notebook 3
[VI.B.3]
8 ¼ x 5 ¼

Finnegans Wake notebook 4
[VI.B.4]
8 ¾ x 6

Finnegans Wake notebook 5
[VI.B.5]
8 ⅜ x 5 ¼

Finnegans Wake notebook 6
[VI.B.6]
8 ⅜ x 5 ¼

Finnegans Wake notebook 7
[VI.B.7]
5 ¾ x 3 ¾

Finnegans Wake notebook 8
[VI.B.8]
6 ¾ x 4 ½

Finnegans Wake notebook 9
[VI.B.9]
4 ¼ x 6 ½

Finnegans Wake notebook 10
[VI.B.10]
Pages 1 and 15
Each 8 ⅜ x 5 ¼

✳ *Finnegans Wake* notebook 10
[VI.B.10]
8 ⅜ x 5 ¼

Finnegans Wake notebook 11
[VI.B.11]
8 ½ x 5 ¼

Finnegans Wake notebook 13
[VI.B.13]
6 ¾ x 4 ¾

Finnegans Wake notebook 14
[VI.B.14]
6 ¾ x 4 ¾

Finnegans Wake notebook 15
[VI.B.15]
7 ⅝ x 15 ⅛

Finnegans Wake notebook 16
[VI.B.16]
8 ⅜ x 5 ½

Finnegans Wake notebook 17
[VI.B.17]
8 ½ x 5 ¼

Finnegans Wake notebook 18
[VI.B.18]
8 ½ x 5 ½

Finnegans Wake notebook 19
[VI.B.19]
6 ¾ x 4 ½

Finnegans Wake notebook 20
[VI.B.20]
8 ½ x 3 ½

Finnegans Wake notebook 21
[VI.B.21]
8 ½ x 5 ¾

Finnegans Wake notebook 22
[VI.B.22]
7 ½ x 4 ¾

Finnegans Wake notebook 23
[VI.B.23]
7 ½ x 5 ⅛

Finnegans Wake notebook 24
[VI.B.24]
8 ½ x 6

Finnegans Wake notebook 26
[VI.B.26]
10 ⅛ x 4

Finnegans Wake notebook 27
[VI.B.27]
7 ¾ x 5 ¼

Finnegans Wake notebook 28
[VI.B.28]
7 ¾ x 5 ½

Finnegans Wake notebook 29
[VI.B.29]
8 ⅜ x 5 ⅝

Finnegans Wake notebook 30
[VI.B.30]
5 ¾ x 3 ¾

Finnegans Wake notebook 31
[VI.B.31]
8 ½ x 5 ¾

Finnegans Wake notebook 32
[VI.B.32]
5 ⅝ x 8 ¾

Finnegans Wake notebook 33
[VI.B.33]
5 ½ x 8 ½

✻ *Finnegans Wake* notebook 34
[VI.B.34]
8 ¼ x 5 ¼

Finnegans Wake notebook 35
[VI.B.35]
8 ¼ x 5 ½

Finnegans Wake notebook 36
[VI.B.36]
7 ¾ x 5 ½

Finnegans Wake notebook 37
[VI.B.37]
7 ⅞ x 5 ½

Finnegans Wake notebook 38
[VI.B.38]
8 ¼ x 5 ⅝

Finnegans Wake notebook 39
[VI.B.39]
4 ¼ x 3

Finnegans Wake notebook 40
[VI.B.40]
8 ¼ x 5 ½

Finnegans Wake notebook 41
[VI.B.41] (same as [VI.C.18])
7 ¾ x 6 ¼

Finnegans Wake notebook 42
[VI.B.42]
5 ½ x 8 ¼

Finnegans Wake notebook 43
[VI.B.43]
5 ¾ x 4

Finnegans Wake notebook 44
[VI.B.44]
8 ¼ x 5 ⅜

Finnegans Wake notebook 45
[VI.B.45]
7 1/2 x 5 ½

Finnegans Wake notebook 46
[VI.B.46]
8 ¾ x 6 ¼

Finnegans Wake notebook 47
[VI.B.47]
5 ⅞ x 3 ¾

Finnegans Wake notebook 48
[VI.B.48]
6 ¾ x 4 ¾

Finnegans Wake Madame Raphael notebook 1
[VI.C.1]
7 ¾ x 6 ¼

Finnegans Wake Madame Raphael notebook 2
[VI.C.2]
7 ¾ x 6 ¼

Finnegans Wake Madame Raphael notebook 3
[VI.C.3]
7 ¾ x 6 ¼

Finnegans Wake Madame Raphael notebook 4
[VI.C.4]
7 ¾ x 6 ¼

Finnegans Wake Madame Raphael notebook 5
[VI.C.5]
7 ¾ x 6 ¼

Finnegans Wake Madame Raphael notebook 6
[VI.C.6]
7 ¾ x 6 ¼

Finnegans Wake Madame Raphael notebook 7
[VI.C.7]
7 ¾ x 6 ¼

Finnegans Wake Madame Raphael notebook 8
[VI.C.8]
7 ¾ x 6 ¼

✶ *Finnegans Wake* Madame Raphael notebook 9
[VI.C.9]
7 ¾ x 6 ¼

Finnegans Wake Madame Raphael notebook 10
[VI.C.10]
7 ¾ x 6 ¼

Finnegans Wake Madame Raphael notebook 11
[VI.C.11]
7 ¾ x 6 ¼

Finnegans Wake Madame Raphael notebook 12
[VI.C.12]
7 ¾ x 6 ¼

Finnegans Wake Madame Raphael notebook 13
[VI.C.13]
7 ¾ x 6 ¼

Finnegans Wake Madame Raphael notebook 14
[VI.C.14]
7 ¾ x 6 ¼

Finnegans Wake Madame Raphael notebook 15
[VI.C.15]
7 ¾ x 6 ¼

✢ *Finnegans Wake* Madame Raphael notebook 16
[VI.C.16]
7 ¾ x 6 ¼

Finnegans Wake Madame Raphael notebook 17
[VI.C.17]
7 ¾ x 6 ¼

Finnegans Wake Madame Raphael notebook 18
[VI.C.18] (same as [VI.B.41])
7 ¾ x 6 ¼

Memorandum notebook
[VIII.C.2]
4 ½ x 2 ¾

Early sigla of *Finnegans Wake*
VI.K.1
6 ½ x 4 ¼

James Joyce's drawing of *Anna Livia Plurabelle*
(siglum) for Sylvia Beach
[VI.K.12]
10 ¾ x 8 ¼

Diagram for *Anna Livia Plurabelle*
[VI.K.6]
10 ¾ x 8 ¼

Early, smaller diagram for *Anna Livia Plurabelle*
[VI.K.5]
8 ¼ x 5 ¼

Issy's alphabet
[VI.K.10]
7 ½ x 5 ⅛

Anna Livia Plurabelle
[VI.F.3]
Ten marked pages
7 ¼ x 5 ½

Anna Livia Plurabelle design
[VI.K.2]
3 ¾ x 6 ¼

Finnegans Wake typescript
[VI.I.1]
Riverrun page
12 ⅛ x 8 ¼

Finnegans Wake
[VI.H.4.a]
Disbound copy with corrections
9 ¾ x 7 x 1 ¾

Finnegans Wake
[VI.H.4.b]
Thirty-one pages of typescript corrections
Each 10 ½ x 8 ¼

"Tim Finigan's Wake"
[IX.A.9]
Typescript
10 ¾ x 8 ⅜

Samuel Beckett to James Joyce, 1929
XI. Beckett to Joyce
Telegram
5 ½ x 4 ½

* Vincent Deane, Daniel Ferrer, and Geert Lernout, editors
The "Finnegans Wake" Notebooks at Buffalo, 12 vols.
Turnhout, Belgium: Brepols Publishers, 2001–2004

Serialization and Later Works

Emended *transition* placard
[VI.G]
19 ¾ x 25 ¼

Emended *transition* placard
[VI.G]
19 ¾ x 25 ¼

Emended *transition* placard
[VI.G]
19 ¾ x 12 ¾

Emended *transition* placard
[VI.G]
ALP glyph in corner
19 ¾ x 12 ¾

Emended *transition* placard
[VI.G]
Dated June 3, 1928
19 ¾ x 12 ¾

Emended *transition* placard
[VI.G]
Three-page section
19 ¾ x 12 ¾

* Samuel Beckett, et al.
Our Exagmination Round His Factification for Incamination of Work in Progress
Paris: Shakespeare and Company, 1929
Copy 67 of 96

Vladimir Dixon to James Joyce, Feburary 9, 1929
XI. Dixon to Joyce [X.A.1]
Holograph letter, four leaves ("Litter of Protest")
Each 10 ½ x 8 ¼

James Joyce
Tales Told of Shem and Shaun
Paris: Black Sun Press, 1929

Black Sun Press contract for *Tales Told of Shem and Shaun*
XVIII.G. Folder 9
Three leaves
Each 10 ⅞ x 8 ½

Correction of Misprints
New York: Viking Press, 1945

* James Joyce, Ford Madox Ford, John Quinn,
and Ezra Pound at Pound's Paris flat, 1923
Launch date of the *Transatlantic Review*
Photograph, black & white (unknown)
8 x 10

* *Two Worlds* I, no. 1 (Sept. 1925)

transition I (April 1927)

Harry Crosby to James Joyce, March 13, 1929
XI. Crosby to Joyce
Holograph letter
6 x 7 ¾

Joyce's suggestions to Padraic Colum
for the introduction to *Anna Livia Plurabelle*
[VI.K.8]
Holograph, three leaves
Each 9 x 6 ⅞

James Joyce
Haveth Childers Everywhere
London: Faber & Faber, 1931

James Joyce
Haveth Childers Everywhere
Paris: Henry Babou and Jack Kahane, 1930;
New York: Fountain Press, 1930

James Joyce
Anna Livia Plurabelle
London: Faber & Faber, 1930

＊ James Joyce
Anna Livia Plurabelle
New York: Crosby Gaige, 1928

James Joyce
Finnegans Wake
London: Faber and Faber, 1939
First edition

Umberto Veruda (Italian, 1868–1904)
Livia Schmitz
Oil on canvas
30 x 24

＊ Publisher's announcement of *Haveth Childers Everywhere*
Paris: Henry Babou and Jack Kahane, 1930
XVIII.G. Folder 16
7 ½ x 5 ⅜

Tor (nationality and dates unknown)
XXII. Folder 3
James Joyce, 1925
Pencil on paper
6 ¾ x 4

Déjeuner *Ulysse*, June 27, 1929. Names penned in by Adrienne Monnier.

James Joyce in Zurich, 1941.